Spoken Cat

ALEXANDRA SELLERS

Spoken Cat

AND RELEVANT FACTORS IN WORLDVIEW

BELLEW · LONDON

BY THE SAME AUTHOR

The Begin Note's Role in Meaning

A Preliminary Grammar of Cat

Tonality in Spoken Cat

Cat Grammar

Thus Spake Zarathustra's Cat

First published in Great Britain 1997

Bellew Publishing Company Limited
8 Balham Hill, London SW12 9EA

ISBN 1 85725 117 2

Typeset by Antony Gray
Printed and bound in Great Britain by
Hartnolls Ltd, Bodmin, Cornwall

to

The One Who

IS

. . . shall I play for you?

Contents

Acknowledgements		8
List of Illustrations		9
A Note from the Author		11
Introduction		13
Key to Pronunciation		17
List of Abbreviations		20

GRAMMAR

ONE	*The personal pronouns. Cat and non-Cat. Adjectives. Adjectival strings. The verb 'to be' and Class One verbs. Some relevant notes on etiquette*	25
TWO	*'Must' and other defective verbs. Forms of greeting. The negative. The adjectival breath. Adverbs. Intensifiers. The verb 'to have' and Class Two verbs*	31
THREE	*Possessives. The negative possessive. The past tense. God. Food. Perfect verbs*	37
FOUR	*The Flattery Voice. Questions. Attributes. The plural. Definite and indefinite*	45
FIVE	*Imperative. The future tense. Direct and indirect objects. Expressions of time. Names*	53
SIX	*Colour Names. Here and there. Here is, there is. This and that. Comparison. Attention*	61
SEVEN	*The Fantasy Voice. Numbers. The subordinate connector. The universal 'it'. Impersonal Class Three verbs*	69
EIGHT	*The Offended Voice. The Gentle Reproach. Early Warning. Effective responses to Early Warning*	77
NINE	*Apology. Situational use of the various levels of apology. The 'Seal of Apology'. The follow-up.*	85

TONALITY

TEN	*Tonality. The Point System*	97
ELEVEN	*The Tonal Shapes. Notation Devices*	99
TWELVE	*TrunCation. Begin-and-End. Middle. Alternate*	101
THIRTEEN	*Extensions. Euphony. Threnody. MagnifiCat*	103
FOURTEEN	*The Begin Notes. Begin Note and Meaning*	105
FIFTEEN	*The Base Note. Establishing the Base Note.*	
	Purr Note and Base Note	107

MUSIC, MYTH AND LEGEND

Music	111
The Legend of Canopus	113
The Nine Blessings	115
Other Legends	120

EINSTEIN'S CAT

A Brief Overview of the Evidence for the Influence of Cats on Human Social, Intellectual and Evolutionary Development from Earliest Historical Times to the Present	123
Appendix A	161
Appendix B	164
Bibliography	166
Lexicon	168

Acknowledgements

The author and publisher wish to thank the following for permission to use the illustrations: Chicago Oriental Institute (Plate I), Madhuvanti Ghose (Plate III), Christine Booth (Plate IV), American Institute of Indian Studies (Plate V), Donald M. Stadtner (Plate VI). The portrait of the author's cat, Johnny, was specially drawn by Philip Snow. Faber and Faber gave permission to quote from *Old Possum's Book of Practical Cats* by T. S. Eliot.

List of Illustrations

PLATES

FRONTIS	*The Goddess Mow. Sumer, 4th millennium* BCE	2
I	*Male figure dancing with lion*	145
II	*Dogfodder illustrating the 'buffalo horn' argument*	148
III	*India. Stone lion with tripod symbol*	148
IV	*Einstein's Cat*	159
V	*India. The Pallava sculpture*	163
VI	*The Pallava sculpture. Detail*	163

FIGURES

1	*Ziggurat school showing the seven levels of classroom*	127
2	*Pottery bowl from Harappa*	128
3	*Sumerian cuneiform, sa'a, Cat*	129
4	*The priestess found at Knossos*	134
5	*Cat on roof of shrine, Knossos*	134
6	*Palace at Knossos with Cat ear ornamentation*	135
7	*Hittite hieroglyphic, 'Hatti', Sacred Pool of Hattusa*	136
8	*Late Egyptian hieroglyphic, 'Khatti'*	136
9	*Linear B, 'Tripod'*	137
10	*Harappan seal. Human figure dancing with two tigers*	138
11	*Caracal Cat*	147
12	*Portrait of Murr, Hoffman's Cat*	155
13	*Portrait of Lyon, Edward Topsell's Cat*	156

9

A Note from the Author

The publiCation of *Cat Grammar*, although it was primarily a textbook for academics, brought home to many members of the public for the first time the enormous breakthrough that has been achieved in the understanding of Cat over the past decade. Since then a great deal of both information and misinformation (not to say *dis*information!) about the language and about Cats[1] has crept into the record, and it is partly with the hope of putting some of the wilder misapprehensions straight that the author has bowed to the growing public demand for an easily absorbed presentation of the language for the layperson.

Cat is a uniquely difficult language for the self-taught. Although there are problems attendant on the production of a language tape, I hope that a cassette will be available in the future to supplement the text. However, the text is designed to stand alone. Students will find the help of a native speaker valuable.

My thanks to all those who wrote to express an interest in such a text, and to those who assisted in its preparation. Dr Irving Finkel at the British Museum somewhat reluctantly advised me on Sumerian cuneiform; Dr Ab de Jong at Hebrew University, Jerusalem, on Cats in Zoroastrianism; Dr Philip Kreyenbroek on the reporting of oral tradition; Dr Alexander McKay at the International Institute in Leiden gave more general advice; and Dr Leigh Lisker at the University of Pennsylvania read the manuscript and made many helpful observations. My thanks also to Dr Andrew George, of the School of Oriental and African Studies, who reconstructed for me, from the English rendering, the lost cuneiform tablet pictured on the cover, and to Madhuvanti Ghose, of the Circle of Inner Asian Art, who drew my attention to the Pallava sculpture.

---

[1] The word 'Cat' will be capitalised throughout the text of this book, in defiance of normal English grammatical rules. My advisers point out that the English 'cat' is not adequate to express the real nature and meaning of the concept, but it was thought that the use of 'HM Cat', although more accurate, would only confuse the reader.

All gave generously of their time. The mistakes are of course my own. I also thank Johnny and Medico, two Cats of (mostly) unwavering loyalty, who tried not to lie to me more than once or twice a day, and then only in small matters or easily detected discrepancies. As usual, without them, nothing could have been achieved

Alexandra Sellers
London, April 1997

Introduction

The language of Cats is as old as what humans call 'the domestiCation of the Cat' (Cats give it quite a different name), doubtless much older, and has survived throughout the period of human historical record apparently with little change to the present day. In spite of its having millions of speakers around the world, there is little dialect variation among native speakers of Cat, and a grasp of Cat as presented in this book will allow you to converse with Cats of most 'breeds'[1] or nations in most areas of the world.

Cat, as has already been discovered by many, is difficult from the beginning. Not only is the tonal element strange to most speakers of Western languages, but in addition the grammar is inseparable from a unique worldview that will challenge many favourite concepts of speakers of human languages. But there is a solution: the more open-minded the student is, the more quickly they will proceed. It is no good taking offence at the imagined prejudices of Cat grammar. It will be far better for students to examine their own prejudices.

A word about the presentation: the 'grammar method' style of teaching a language is out of fashion at the moment, and indeed, many English speakers have never learned the grammar even of their own language; but in Cat there are important reasons for the methodical presentation of the structure and rules of the language. The language is sacred to Cats, and errors in its use are not tolerated. Grammar mistakes are a particularly dangerous pitfall which must at all costs be avoided; and unless the Cat worldview's effect on the grammar is clearly explained, the student, as well as becoming thoroughly confused, runs the risk of offending Cats, with perhaps profound effects on any subsequent learning. The student must be, and is in the following pages, warned of risky ground. Thus no apology is offered for presenting the language in what some may see as an outmoded format.

---

[1] This term is offensive to most Cats.

THE PRESENTATION

Each chapter in Part One is constructed to the same format. A short passage presenting a simple, everyday situation is followed by a vocabulary list and discussion of the various grammar points raised in the passage, including an explanation of the cultural concepts which may underpin them. Practical spoken and written exercises are then presented.

Part Two must be studied in conjunction with Part One. Here you will learn that Cat is a tonal language – in fact, the most highly tonal of all mammalian languages, and perhaps of all languages of sound. A musical ear is a distinct advantage. The very musical, and especially the violinists among the human population, will find the task of learning Cat significantly easier than the general population.[2] Part Two, then, briefly explains the nature of tonality, and the specific form it takes in Cat. It discusses and explains the Seven Tonal Shapes and the Six Begin Notes, and briefly mentions their role in meaning. Although it is placed second in the text, *Part Two must be thoroughly absorbed before Part One can be put into use, and before any attempt is made to speak the language to a Cat.*

Self-taught students will find the area of tonality daunting at first, especially in the absence of a native speaker. Do not be discouraged: with a little determination, and the use of the charts and a musical instrument such as a violin, it is quite possible for ordinary human beings to learn enough Cat to communiCate with their resident Cats.

A word of warning must go along with any handbook or course of instruction in Cat: *be wary of believing what you are told by even the most beloved of Cats.* The attitude of Cats to what we call 'lying' is little understood by humans, who must learn to resist applying human standards to the matter. That there is no word for *truth* in Cat is already well known; what is less generally known, and the impliCations little appreciated, is that there is also no word for *lie*. Unless, of course (and this must always be borne in mind), Cats are lying to us in this matter.

Cats, it now appears, simply say anything they like. The layperson should bear this fact in mind in every communiCation with a Cat. It is extremely unlikely, for example, that any ordinary 'house'[3] Cat would have access to information on a conspiracy of Cats to take over the world, even if such a conspiracy existed. The wise will think carefully before calling

---

[2] The tone deaf, on the other hand, will be entirely unable to learn Cat, and should make no attempt to speak it at any time. The risk of offending a Cat through error is so high it may be called a certainty.

[3] This term is offensive to Cats.

the Prime Minister or MI6 with any such information a Cat may impart. And before you go off to Land's End to dig at the foot of a linden tree, pause to ask yourself how 'your' Cat knows where the Inca treasure was hidden.

In short, you should be cautious about acting on information received from a Cat, unless such information concerns the Cat's personal wishes or needs. You will learn later in this book how to detect, and the proper ways to respond to, what is called the Fantasy element in Cat.

But even if you do get sent off on one or two embarrassing adventures before this lesson sinks in, you are certain to find the study of Cat exciting and rewarding. My admiration goes out to all those dediCated enough to undertake this exacting study on their own, and I wish you every success with Spoken Cat.

Key to Pronunciation

THE ALPHABET

Cat as a language is not best suited to being transcribed in the Roman alphabet, and indeed, for scholarly purposes an entirely new alphabet has been developed. But for the purposes of self-teaching, it was thought that the disadvantages of the Roman alphabet would be more than offset by the ease of reading; and so an attempt has been made to cast the sounds of Cat into the Roman alphabet – as closely as possible to the sounds represented by those letters in English. Three sounds with no reasonable equivalent in English writing are represented by other marks.

Some of the differences between sounds in Cat – particularly all the sounds clumped under the letter **r** by the English speaker – are often indetectable to the human ear at first, and this may lead you to make some rather startling errors when you begin (see Chapter Nine, Apology). However, as you listen more closely to native speakers, your ear will soon begin to detect the subtle but very real differences in sound. It may take much longer before you are able to reproduce them accurately, but you will often be comprehensible even through such errors, much as Japanese speakers of English are comprehensible to English native speakers in spite of their **r** and **l** confusion.

THE CONSONANTS

There are 15 consonants in Cat. In written form in this book they are represented as follows:

    b   –   as in 'brow' but much less stressed
    f   –   as in 'fuss' but with the teeth placed lightly **behind** the
            lower lip, and not on top of it
    h   –   as in 'huh', a short sigh
    m   –   lighter than the English sound – the lips are together
            but are opened as the sound begins, so there is no 'hum'
    n   –   as for **m**, a very light sound

p – as in 'praise'; see **b**

r – simple English untrilled **r**, as in 'brawl'

rr – trilled **r**. The nearest human equivalent of this sound is formed when the tongue flutters on the hard palate.[1]

R – uvular **r**, as in French 'tresor'

RR – heavily rolled uvular **r**

t – as with **b** and **p**

w – the sound made between the **h** and **a** in English 'ohh ahh'

^ – glottal breath

` – glottal stop

' – soft or 'breathed' glottal stop

THE VOWELS

a – as in English 'flap'

aa – elongated **a**, as when humans imitate sheep ('baa')

e – as in 'left'

ee – long, as in 'peep'

i – as in 'blip', but very short

o – between 'box' and 'roll', short

u – as in 'cup' but very short

aw – as in 'oh'

ow – as in 'down', never as in 'furrow'

ew – as in 'ewe'

NOTES ON PRONUNCIATION

1 Vowels which follow **r** and **rr** are generally nasalised.

2 As in English, the sound represented by English 'w' and 'oo' is sometimes a consonant and sometimes a vowel. As a consonant it is an unstressed sound, unless it appears after the diphthong 'ow', when it acquires the force of dupliCation, as in **merowwap**, 'to be hungry'.

3 **p**, **t** and **m** are never exploded when they appear at the end of a word. The sound stops as the lips come together, as if it were swallowed.

4 **m** might be described as a hum of very short duration. Never put a vowel sound between **m** and a following consonant, or before the **m**; **mboh**, for example, is not pronounced 'emboh', nor 'meboh'. To practise this sound, pronounce English 'umbrella' without the **u**.

---

[1] Note that the notation of three or more **rs** (in Fourth Level Offence and above) indiCates an elongated *untrilled* palatal **r**.

5 **n** as with **m**

6 **ow** is pronounced from a very open-mouth position, sliding quickly down to the closed position

7 There is an overall nasality to almost all Cat utterances which it is impossible to indiCate in the Roman alphabet, but which it is not difficult for human speakers to produce. Though North Americans, generally speaking, should make no attempt to increase their own naturally occurring nasality, other English speakers can attain this effect by 'talking through the nose'.

List of Abbreviations

JCAT	Journal of Cat as Tutor
AJCS	American Journal of Cat Studies
CH	La Chatte
CK	Col haKhatoul
UBCAT	University of British Columbia CAT
KS	Katzenstudieren
JRAS	Journal of the Royal Asiatic Society
Possum	T. S. Eliot, Old Possum's Book of Practical Cats
Hdt.	Herodotus, The Histories

It is manifestly evident that there is among them a full and entire communication, and that they understand each other.

MICHEL DE MONTAIGNE

PART ONE

Grammar

Chapter One

The personal pronouns
Cat and non-Cat
Adjectives
Adjectival strings
The verb 'to be' and Class One verbs
Some relevant notes on etiquette

mow[1]	The Cat
mow [2] **'aow row mew.**	The little Cat is cold.
ma`row 'Rowow pwah row.	The pretty coat is wet.
uh rrow uh rowb pwah row.	The whiskers and tail are wet.
mow 'RRaow row.	The Cat is lonely.
mow merowwap.	She is hungry.

VOCABULARY

'aow(b1)[3]	little, small	**mRaow**(b3)	food
'Rowow(d2)	pretty,	**pwah**(c7)	wet
	beautiful	**row**(a1, f 7)	to be
'RRaow((a2)	lonely	**rowb**(b6)	tail
ma`row(b3)	coat/fur	**rrow**(b4)	whiskers
merowwap(a1, f 7)[4]	to be hungry	**uh**(a7)	and, also
mew(c7)	cold		
mow(a1)	Cat, Cat Presence, Higher Being		

1 THE PERSONAL PRONOUNS

There are two sets of personal pronouns, those for use by Cats and those for 'non-Cats'. Humans fall into the latter Category.

Cat

I/we	**mow** (a1)		
you (Cat)	**mowuh** (a4)	*you* (non-Cat)	**ma`**(f 7)
she/he/they (C)	**mow** (a1)	*she/he/it/they* (nC)	**ma`**(f 7)

Non-Cat

I/we	**ma`**(f 7)		
you (nC)	—	*you* (C)	**mow** (a1)
she/he/it/they (nC)	**ma`**(f 7)	*she/he/they* (C)	**mow** (a1)[5]

[1] This is a lullaby that mother Cats sing to their young.

[2] Capitals are not used to mark the beginning of sentences because of the potential for confusion between **R** and **r**.

[3] The letter and number in brackets refer to the pronunciation code, called the Begin Note – Tonal Shape (BNTS) Code. See Part Two.

[4] The first BNTS refers to Cats; the second to non-Cats.

[5] Rare. See under Notes.

a. You will have noticed that there are only three forms – **mow, mowuh** and **ma`** – to serve the seven English pronouns **I, you, she, he, it, we, they.** There is no such thing as a pronoun in Cat. The word **mow**(a1) literally means 'Cat Presence/Higher Being'. Thus it serves as **I/we** when a Cat is speaking, and **you** when a Cat is being addressed. Although, as mentioned in the section on tonality, Begin Note A carries overtones of plurality, **mow**, Cat Presence, nevertheless exists only in the singular. The much-bruited idea that 'all Cats use the royal We all the time'[6] is, therefore, utter nonsense.

b. There is no distinction between the first person Cat (I/we) and the third person (she, he, they). Cats rarely speak to humans of other Cats; when they do they will use **mow**(a1) and the Cat's 'particular'[7] name.

c. **ma`**, on the other hand, means simply, 'non-Cat'. Thus a Cat may use it for **you** as well as for **she, he, it, they** when speaking to or of non-Cats. In your own speech, this form means both **I/we** and, when you are speaking of another non-Cat, **she, he, it, they.**

d. You will find these points simple to grasp if you learn to think in Cat terms (Cat Presence, also Cat Presence, non-Cat) rather than in pronouns. The Cat grammatical worldview is not very different in this regard from the widespread human tendency to divide the world grammatically into masculine, feminine and neuter.

e. You may perhaps hear the third person non-Cat, **ma`**, used by Cats as the 'you' form to other Cats. *Never*, under any circumstances, be tempted to use it in this way yourself, even in error. It does not mean 'you' or 'they' here; in this form it is an insult and must be left to Cats to use among themselves.

f. Note that there is no second person form for non-Cats to use to non-Cats. *It is an offence for humans to speak to one another in Cat.*[8] (See Chapter Nine, Apology.) Use English or another language. As Cats say, 'Dog is good enough.'

---

[6] Primarily Dogfodder, 'The nature of the A note and the conscious royal prerogative of Cats expressed by the A note–F note split with particular regard to the use among Cats of the pseudo-pronoun mow to designate the self', *JCAT*, Vol.3, No. iv, pp. 252–85. He overlooks the distinction between tonal pattern 1 and tonal pattern 4. Furthermore, plurality elsewhere in Cat is clearly considered a negative phenomenon. The use of a plural by Cats would therefore be taken as a sign of humility, not arrogance. But the fact is that **mow** (a1) is not a plural, and therefore bears no relation to the royal We in English. Thus the whole argument falls to the ground.

[7] For an account of the levels of Cat names, see Eliot, 'The Naming of Cats' in *Possum*, p. 1

[8] It has become acceptable in classroom situations, but note that in all such human-to-human exchanges, one human must speak as a Cat.

2 'CAT' AND 'NON-CAT'

Cat is a language that uses different *levels* of speech. You have already met the only two levels you will have to learn, Cat and non-Cat.[9] These levels are of the highest importance from the very beginning, because ***you may not simply repeat what a Cat says when you are learning a phrase.***

For example, **mow**(a1) **merowwap**(a1), when spoken by a Cat, translates colloquially, 'I'm hungry!' Its literal meaning, however, is 'the Cat Presence hungers'. The same phrase, when spoken by you, would mean, 'You are hungry', and may only be used to address a Cat. It would be considered impertinent of you to inform a Cat of your own hunger, but should you do so, you would say **ma`**(f 7) **merowwap**(f 7), literally, 'non-Cat hungers'. This phrase would be virtually meaningless to a Cat, as it would appear to be a peculiarly uninteresting statement about the general nature of non-Cat.

The two levels of the language will henceforward be signalled by C and nC in this textbook. The same two divisions will refer to the speakers. The context should make clear which is meant. In the following chart:

C

leave me alone (nC)!   –   **maaa`**(f 7)

maaa`** is the form for a Cat addressing a non-Cat. Thus the **C** indiCates that the form is for **use by Cats**, and the (nC) that it is the form for **addressing non-Cats.`

NOTE: The popular idea that these different levels of speech in Cat involve status is mistaken. No judgement whatsoever is implied by the distinction between Cat and non-Cat. The distinction is entirely *grammatical*.

3 ADJECTIVES

An adjective modifies a noun. That is to say, it is a word used to describe some person, place, thing or idea. In the phrase, 'Dogfodder's ideas are unsound', *unsound* is an adjective[10] modifying the noun *ideas*.

1   Adjectives may precede or follow the noun they modify, or both. They may also stand alone.

`aow mow	–	little Cat
rowb `Rowow	–	pretty tail

---

[9] There are other levels of Cat, but these all exist as sub-levels within the Cat level – that is, they are solely for Cats conversing with other Cats – and are of no importance to ordinary human students of the language. They involve a much wider variety of Tonal Shapes and Begin Notes than you will study in this book, and are extremely difficult for humans. Much of such communiCation apparently involves insult.

[10] Specifically, of course, a subjective completion of the copula verb.

4 ADJECTIVAL STRINGS

When two or more adjectives are used in conjunction, they are joined by
uh – 'and'.

mew uh 'RRaow uh 'aow mow   –   cold, lonely, little Cat

A noun may also be bracketed by adjectives. In this case **uh** is not needed,
as the noun takes its place.

'Rowow mow 'aow   –   beautiful little Cat

5 THE VERB 'TO BE'

	C	nC
I am/we are	**mow**(a1) **row**(a1)	**ma`**(f 7) **row**(f 7)
you (C) *are*	**mowuh**(a4) **row**(a1)	**mow**(a1) **row**(a1)
you (nC) *are*	**ma`**(f 7) **row**(f 7)	–
she/he/they (C) *are*	**mow**(a1) **row**(a1)	**mow**(a1) **row**(a1)
she/he/it/they (nC) *are*	**ma`**(f 7) **row**(f 7)	**ma`**(f 7) **row**(f 7)

CLASS ONE VERBS

a. Verbs indiCating state of being rather than action are called Class One
verbs. They follow the pattern of the verb **row**: Cat verbs take the BNTS
a1 and non-Cat verbs the BNTS **f 7**.

mow merowwap(a1)   –   you(C) are hungry

b. All inanimate objects and non-sentient nature take the Cat form of the
verb.

mRaow mew(c7) **row**(a1)   –   the food is cold

6 WRITTEN EXERCISE

Find the words for the following (choose the non-Cat level of speech):

1   Cat.
2   You (C) are pretty.
3   The little Cat is hungry.
4   You (C) are cold and wet.
5   Food.

7 COMPREHENSION EXERCISE[11]

mow(a1). **mow**(a1) **'Rowow**(d2) **row**(a1). **mow**(a1) **merowwap**(a1).
mRaow(b3) **mew**(c7) **row**(a1). **rrow**(b4) **row**(a1) **pwah**(c7).

---

[11] For a translation of this and subsequent exercises, see Appendix B.

8 PRACTICAL EXERCISES WITH A NATIVE SPEAKER[12]

For your first session, use ordinary methods of gaining the Cat's attention: a bit of cheese or a deliCate scratching motion on whatever part of the anatomy the Cat presents. Adopt a relaxed posture.

If the Cat pays no attention, ***do not make a kissing or sucking noise.*** This generally gains the Cat's *negative* attention, and will be counter-productive. Simply abandon your efforts and try another time.

When you have the Cat's attention, quietly repeat the expression **ma`**, on Begin Note F and Tonal Pattern 7. This indiCates your willingness to be of service. ***Your attitude should above all be humble.***

Do not expect a response at once. The Cat may need time to overcome its surprise. Say the word two or three times and then return to ordinary human/Cat communiCation. The Cat will now find ways to indiCate what service might be acceptable at this time. Be sure to oblige.

[12] To be omitted by those without access to a native speaker or a classroom teacher.

Chapter Two

'Must' and other defective verbs
Forms of greeting
The negative
The adjectival breath
Adverbs
Intensifiers
The verb 'to have' and Class Two verbs

SCENE:

A human meets the neighbour's Cat in the garden.
The following conversation ensues.

CAT:	**mow**(a1).	How do you do?
HUMAN:	**mow. ma`**(f 7).	How do you do, Honoured Cat? I am at liberty just at the moment. Can I be of service?
CAT:	**ma` mupRup**(f 7) **birr**(b5) **birr pirp**(c4)	A dish of cream, if you would be so kind.
HUMAN:	**birr birr ma` bra!**	Cream coming up!

The human brings a dish of cream and offers it.
The Cat drinks the cream.

CAT:	**mbruuh**(a5)	Thank you!
HUMAN:	**ma` RRow**(a1). **ma`?**	My pleasure, certainly. Is there anything else?

The Cat leaves.

VOCABULARY

birr(b5)	milk	**mbruuh**(a5)(C)	thank you
birr(b5)**birr**[1]	cream	**mi'ao**(a4)	garden
bra(c4)(nC)	to work; lift, carry, fetch; do	**nmbruh**(f 7)	unpleasant
		pirp(c4)(nC)	to bring; offer, make an offering to
ma` RRow(a1)(nC)	thank you		
mbruh(b5)	nice, pleasant		
mbruuh(a5)	pleased	**ruh**(b4, c4)	to intend, mean

1 THE VERB 'MUST'

C

you (nC) *must*	–	**mupRup**(f 7)[2]
she/he/it/they (nC) *must*	–	**mupRup**

nC

I/we must	–	**mupRup**
it/they (nC) *must*	–	**mupRup**

---

[1] Note the section on intensifiers below.

[2] Note that, as a Class One verb, *must* is considered a state of being. Cats do not experience such a state of being. Thus the verb is defective.

a. mupRup is a defective verb. There is no form of **mupRup** to use to a Cat. Never use any form of this verb to give a Cat an order. It is a grammatical error of the gravest nature. (See Chapter 9, Apology.)

b. mupRup is followed by the verb in its normal conjugated form.

mupRup bra(c4)   –   please do it![3]

DEFECTIVE VERBS

There are certain verbs which, like **mupRup**, exist only in the non-Cat form. Class One defective verbs follow the **mupRup** pattern. In this book they are notated (f 7)(nC).

2 FORMS OF GREETING

As you have learned in Chapter One, **mow**(a1), the word used by Cats as the first person pronoun (I/we), means 'Cat Presence'. This word is also the most common Cat greeting, generally used by Cats upon entering a room. The word may never be used in this way by a human, since the substance of it is to announce the arrival of Cat Presence. It may be used in *response* to a Cat greeting, then signifying, 'I acknowledge Cat Presence.'

You may find yourself in a situation where you wish to greet a Cat who has not previously greeted you. Generally speaking, this is a social solecism unless the Cat addressed is hungry.[4] However, the rules here, as elsewhere, are looser than they used to be. In such circumstances, to avoid giving offence, it is best to say **ma`**(f 7), 'non-Cat'. In this context the word signifies 'servant' and implies a readiness to engage in some duty that will be pleasing to the Cat.

The most polite (and welcome) form of address is the well-known **mRaow**(b3),[5] but students are reminded that this word means literally 'food', and should only be used when it is to be followed by a real offer of food.

3 THE NEGATIVE

a. The negative is formed by adding the sound **n** before the part of speech to be negatived. English speakers use the sound whenever they shorten the word 'and', as in the phrase 'It's raining Cats 'n' dogs.'[6] In Cat, the

---

[3] Lit. 'you (nC) must do it', but in this and similar contexts the Cat should not be seen as giving an order, but merely commenting, as it were, on the state of being of the human. 'I know that your (good) nature compels you' is closer to the state of mind of a Cat using this verb.

[4] But see Eliot, 'The Ad-dressing of Cats', for an alternate view: 'Myself, I do not hold with that. I say, you should ad-dress a Cat.' *Possum*, p. 54f.

[5] See Chapter Four for another acceptable greeting.

[6] This phrase is deeply offensive to Cats. It is used here through necessity. See Chapter 9, Apology.

sound is shorter. There is no BNTS for **n** because its Tonal Shape consists entirely of its Begin Note, which it takes from the word it precedes.

nmow(a1)   –   non-Cat[7]

The negative may be attached to any part of speech. **mRaow nrow** and **nmRaow row** both signify, 'It's inedible.'

b. Negative turns of phrase figure prominently in the speech of non-Cats, and you should be sure to learn it. It is particularly useful for apology, as in:

ma`(f 7) **nruh**(f 7)   –   I didn't mean it

4 THE ADJECTIVAL BREATH

a. Adjectives carry a 'non-Cat' signifier when they are used to describe a sentient being other than a Cat. This is an almost silent breath added to the end of the adjective. It is indiCated by the sign ^.

mbruh^ ma`   –   nice human

b. This sound also appears on its own, when it indiCates a high degree of positive interest in a non-Cat – ^^. In this rarely used form, delivered with the mouth wide open, it has become popularly known as 'the silent miaow', although it is more properly called the glottal squeak. It is generally used to disarm humans.[8]

c. The adjectival breath is difficult for most humans to pronounce, but it is seldom necessary because of the indifference Cats feel towards any discussion of non-Cats. Remember that Cats have a great deal on their minds (see Part 4, Einstein's Cat). Keep your use of non-Cat adjectives to a minimum.

ma` 'aow^ row(f 7)   –   she (nC) is small[9]

NOTE: Inanimate objects and non-sentient nature[10] do not require the adjectival breath.

birr mew(c7) **row**(a1)   –   the milk is cold

---

[7] This word is not in general use among Cats. Most Cats feel that the word **mow**(a1) is sacred, and cannot be used in any way in reference to a non-Cat. Some Cats may use it to a favoured human as a sign of particular benevolence. It is given here as a grammatical example only. The accepted form for non-Cat is given above: **ma`**(f 7).

[8] The open-mouthed hiss ^^^^^ is etymologically related; it indiCates high degree of negative interest in anything.

[9] **mah**(f 7), 'Quite' (Eng) or 'Really' (NA) is often the response to this sort of unnecessary statement, if a Cat hears it at all. While the word expresses a minimal degree of interest, is cannot be translated, as Dogfodder suggests, by 'ho hum'.

[10] Rechter suggests that mice, birds and other *edible* sentient creatures do not take the adjectival breath. This would only be in a case where a Cat was visualising the bird as already non-sentient, however. It is akin to omitting the use of the future tense where intent is high, as in the French *j'arrive!*

5 ADVERBS

There is no distinction between adjectives and adverbs.

mow mieh(d1) **row**   –   the Cat is dainty
mow mieh(d1) **rro**   –   the Cat washes daintily

6 INTENSIFIERS

There is no universal intensifier in Cat equivalent to the English 'very'. An adjective or adverb is intensified in two ways, doubling and bracketing.

'Rowow(d2) **'Rowow mow**(a1)   –   very pretty cat
                                      (lit. pretty pretty Cat) *or*

'Rowow mow 'Rowow   –   (lit. pretty Cat pretty)
mow mowruh(b4) **arp**(b4)   –   she runs incredibly fast
    mowruh

7 THE VERB 'TO HAVE'

	C	nC
I/we have	**mow**(a1) **row**(b4)	**ma`**(f 7) **row**(c4)
you (C) *have*	**mowuh**(a4) **row**(b4)	**mow**(a1) **row**(b4)
you (nC) *have*	**ma`**(f 7) **row**(c4)	—
she/he has/they (C) *have*	**mow**(a1) **row**(b4)	**mow**(a1) **row**(b4)
she/he/it/they (nC) *have*	**ma`**(f 7) **row**(c4)	**ma`**(f 7) **row**(c4)

Note that the consonant–vowel cluster is the same as for the verb 'to be', **row**. But here there is a different Begin Note and Tonal Shape, and therefore there is no confusion in meaning.

CLASS TWO VERBS

All action verbs follow the pattern of the verb **row**(b4), to have. They are called Class Two verbs. Cat verbs take the BNTS b4 and non-Cat verbs the BNTS c4.

CLASS TWO DEFECTIVE VERBS

As with Class One verbs, certain Class Two verbs exist only in the non-Cat form. These describe action performed exclusively by non-Cats. They are notated (c4)(nC).

ma` bra(c4) **birr**   –   I (nC) am fetching milk

8 COMPREHENSION EXERCISE

birr row(a1) **mbruh. pwah ma`row mbruh nrow**(a1). **mow 'aow row**(b4) **rowb 'aow. mupRup birr pirp.**

9 PRACTICAL EXERCISES WITH A NATIVE SPEAKER

Choose a moment when the Cat is in the kitchen.[11] Stand by the refrigerator or a cupboard where food is stored. Say **mRaow**(b3) quietly once or twice. Carefully note the Cat's response. If she says **birr**(b5) or **birr birr**, respond with the appropriate food. If you cannot clearly understand the response, any titbit or snack of which the Cat is particularly fond may now be offered.

Practise this exercise as often as you wish.

---

[11] This is best done when it is *not* the Cat's regular mealtime.

Chapter Three

Possessives
The negative possessive
The past tense
God
Food
Perfect verbs

The Legend of BRRow and 'Aa[1]
bRRow(d1) uh(a7) 'aa(d1)

bRRow(d1) berah(a1) bRRow(b4). mew(d4) bRRow(d1) mRRow(b4).
'aa(d1) mrow(b4) bRRow(d1) ruh(a7) mRRaow(a3)[2] 'aa(c7) Row(a4)
maow(b4).

    mew(a4) **'aa miaow(b4):** *mew*(d4) *mow*(a1) *pra*(b7) *mraow*(b4) *uh*(a7)
irr(a5) *mRRah*(a4) *row*(b4). *m'mow*(a1) *row*(a1). *mowuh*(a4) *pra*(a7)
nmow(b4) *m'mow mRRah*(a4).[3]

    bRRow(d1) mow(b4) m' 'aa(d1) mRRah(a4). 'aa(d1) bRRow(a1).

    'aa(d1) miaow(b4): *mow*(a1) *pra*(c7) *bRRow*(b4)!

    bRRow(d1) rro(b4) rowb(b6). bRRow(d1) broh(b4) mRRaow(a3)
nrow(b4), broh(b4) 'aa pra(c7) bRRow(b4).

    bRRow(d1) bRRow(a1).

    bRRow(d1) miaow(b4): *bRRow*(a6) *mbruh*(b5) *row*. *mow*(a1) *uh*(a7)
ar(a1) *bRRow*(b4) *ruh*(a7) *m' 'aa bRRow*(a6)!

VOCABULARY

'a(a7)	if	**mow**(b4)(C)	to eat
'aa(d1)	'Aa	**mraow**(b4, c4)	to hunt
'aa(c7)	on, in	**maowr**(a2, a4)	salmon/flesh
berah(a1, f 7)	to like	**mRRah**(a4)	titbit, snack
broh(b4, c4)	to see	**mRRaow**(a3)	testicles
broh(a4)	eye	**mRRow**(b4)(C)	to sleep,
bRRow(a1, f 7)	to laugh[4]		commune with
bRRow(a6)	joke, trick		Mow[5]
bRRow(b4)(C)	to play tricks	**pra**(c7)	already, before,
maow(b4, c4)	to place, put		yesterday, 'the
mrow(b4)(C)	to take		time before'
mew(a4)	(in the)	**prrew** (a2, a4)	mouse/meat
	morning	**pwah**(f 7)	water
mew(d4)	night, at night	**Row**(a4)	bowl, dish
miaow(b4)(C)	to talk, say	**rro**(b4, c4)	to wash, clean
miew(a2, a4)	tuna/flesh	**ruh**(a7)	like, similar to

---

[1] For a full English rendering of this story, consult Part Three, pp. 120–1.

[2] 'BRRow's testicles'. Parts of the body are not signified through the possessive. See Chapter Five, Attributes.

[3] 'Do not eat my titbits' (lit. 'You have not eaten my titbits'). This use of the past as an imperative is for Cat-to-Cat communiCation *only*, and would be ungrammatical if used by a human. See Chapter Five, Imperatives.

[4] Note that 'to laugh' is a state of being, not an action.

[5] 'To sleep' is a Class Two perfect verb. This is not an exception to the rule. Sleep performed by Cats is considered active.

1 POSSESSIVES

a. The Possessive Particle

Possession is indiCated by the addition of the particle **m'** to the possessor. The thing possessed follows[6] the possessor. The particle **m'** adopts the Begin Note of the word it modifies.

> **m'mow**(a1) **Row**(a4)   –   the Cat's dish
> **m' 'aa**(d1) **bRRow**(a6)   –   'Aa's joke

The possessive particle may only be attached to the nouns **mow** and **mowuh** or to a Cat's name. *It is never used to indiCate possession by a non-Cat.*

b. Possession by non-Cats – the Negative Possessive

Although in practice many Cats do recognise ownership by humans, grammatically there is no precise way to indiCate that a non-Cat owns anything. Non-Cat possession is implied in the negative possessive 'not belonging to Cat'.[7] There are good historical reasons for this, which have little to do with popular notions of 'Cats feeling they own the world'. Cats do not feel any such thing. Remember the proverb, **'a m'mow**(a1) **row, m'mow**(d4) **row; 'a m'mow**(a1) **nrow, m'mow**(d4) **row** – 'If it is mine, it is God's; if it is not mine, it is God's.'[8]

Generally speaking, you will not need to indiCate particular non-Cat ownership to a Cat. Remember that Cats are not very interested in such details. Where you are absolutely certain that such information is essential to a Cat, there are other ways than the grammatical possessive to indiCate it.

> **mRaow**(b3) **m'mow**   –   the food is not yours; it is Blacky's
>   **nrow Blacky**   (lit. the food is not yours – Blacky)[9]

Here the statement of non-ownership by the Cat is followed by the name of the actual owner.[10]

---

[6] Sometimes, for considerations of style, the possessed object may precede the possessor, but this is not usual in ordinary conversation.

[7] Another (very recent) form, **m'ma`**, with the literal meaning, 'belonging to non-Cat', has been noted, but this is a neologism, which only the most liberal of Cats is likely to use. Do not expect it even from a Cat who is very fond of you. No related form **m'ma`** exists for use by non-Cats. It would be an offence for you to indiCate positive ownership of anything. (See Chapter Nine, Apology)

[8] Elsewhere mistranslated as, 'If it is mine, it is mine; if it is not mine, it is mine.' See Dogfodder, 'Mine, mine and not-yours: problems with the possessive' in *JCAT*, Vol 9, No. i, pp. 11–19. Dogfodder's attested tone-deafness is a barrier to his comprehension of Cat speech, never more grotesquely apparent than here, where he completely misses the distinction between a1 and d4!

[9] Here, of course, Blacky is not a Cat. Where Blacky is a Cat the form will be **mRaow m'mow Blacky row** – 'the food is Blacky's'.

[10] It should be noted that most Cats would consider the addition of the name redundant,

c. The Possessive Pronoun Adjectives[11]

C

my, mine	**m'mow**(a1)		
your, yours (C)	**m'mowuh**(a4)	*your, yours* (nC)	**nm'mow**(a1)[12]
their, theirs (C)	**m'mow**(a1)	*its, theirs* (nC)	**nm'mow**(a1)

nC

my, mine	**nm'mow**(a1)	*your, yours* (C)	**m'mow**(a1)
its, theirs (nC)	**nm'mow**(a1)	*their, theirs* (C)	**m'mow**(a1)

m'mow mRRah(a4) – your (C) titbits (also 'Cat's titbits')
m'mow mRRah – my (C) titbits

The possessive pronoun is not always used. Where possession is understood, it may be omitted.

bRRow rro mRRaow – BRRow cleaned (his) sexual parts.[13]

2 THE PAST TENSE

Cats are rarely concerned about any time other than the present. What humans call the past tense[14] is indiCated by putting the past particle **pra**(c7), 'already, before, yesterday, the time before', before the verb.

bRRow mRRaow(a3) **pra brap**(b4) – BRRow ate his testicles

Where it is not required for sense, it may be omitted.

mow mRRah(a4) **brap** – the Cat ate the titbits *or*
(the Cat is eating the titbits.)

3 GOD

To Cats, God is a Cat. This fact is an intrinsic part of the language, and the concept is an important one to any student of Cat. The word for God, **mow**(d4),[15] will be seen to have the same consonant–vowel cluster as the word for Cat and the first person pronoun, with a different Begin Note

---

and possibly insulting. (See Chapter Nine, Apology.) That the food is not for the Cat is sufficiently unwelcome information. The notion that food *by right* belongs to someone else is grammatically so ridiculous as to be almost incomprehensible.

[11] Strictly speaking, these are neither pronouns nor adjectives, but rather nouns with the possessive particle attached. But the chart may be of use to non-native speakers.
[12] Literally, 'not belonging to Cat'.
[13] This in any case is not a possessive relationship, but an attribute. See Chapter Five.
[14] Human perception of time is defective.
[15] Literally, of course, 'Goddess'. For an ancient Sumerian view of Mow, see Frontispiece.

and Tonal Shape. As you will see in the section on Begin Notes, the D Begin Note (BN D) implies particular femaleness, that is, over and above what might be called the general femaleness of everything.

BN D further carries the impliCation of unity, oneness, while BN A implies diversity. This curious (to humans) reference to the 'personal I' Cat Presence as diversity, and the 'overall' Cat Presence as unity is hard for us, but not apparently for Cats, to comprehend on a metaphysical or philosophical level. It is made more complex by the fact that, as will explained in the section on Tonality, BN D also implies and includes BN A (and not vice versa).

Thus it will be seen that the word **mow**(d4) carries a multitude of virtually untranslatable connotations, which might in English be incompletely expressed as 'I All and One (the Divine Great She) Cat Presence'.

MOW AND HUMANS

The understood 'I' component of the word **mow** makes the use of the word a difficult area for humans. There are Cat free-thinkers who accept that the 'All and One' component of Godhead includes all sentient beings as well as non-sentient nature (which is included as a matter of course). Such free-thinkers point out that although the word arose at a time and place where no sentient species other than Cat existed, it was meant as a universal concept. Thus, they say, even humans have the right to express themselves as part of divinity.

Cat purists, however – and they are in the majority – point out that the third-person pronoun **ma'**(f 7) implies a level of diversity approaching chaos, and therefore non-Cats do not partake of the divinity shared by Cats. A Cat holding this belief will be deeply offended by any attempt on your part to discuss Mow, because you by your nature are incapable of using the word.[16] You are advised to be very, very sure that a Cat is a free-thinker before undertaking any such discussion, and indeed, you ought not to attempt anything of this nature until you are far more fluent in Cat than this book can make you. (See Chapter 9, Apology.)

---

[16] Yet it is clear that pre-Cataclysmic societies – the ancient Sumerians, for example – were encouraged to worship Mow. Bright, in 'Is collective Cat memory long enough?', *UBCAT*, Vol. V, No. 1, pp. 13–46, argues that the prejudice against human use of the word **mow**(d4) is a very late development.

4 FOOD

Much as English makes a distinction between *cow* and *beef*, Cat always makes a distinction between potential food, which is still living, and the meat obtained from it. Thus **maowr**(a4), 'salmon', indiCates that which comes out of a tin, while **maowr**(a2) refers to the living fish.

As you learned in Chapter One, all non-sentient nature, and therefore inert forms of food, take the Cat form of the verb. This is partly because the closer something is to being eaten by a Cat, the closer it is to absorption in Godhead. A second and more significant reason is that food is generally seen as an offering to Mow, and takes on virtue.

Food which is still living, of course, takes the non-Cat form of the verb.

maowr(a4) **'aa Row**(a4) **row**(a1) — the salmon (flesh) is in the bowl

maowr(a2) **'aa pwah**(f 7) **row**(f 7) — the (living) salmon is in the water

5 PERFECT VERBS

Just as some verbs (defective verbs, Chapter Two) can only be conjugated in the non-Cat form, so there are certain verbs which can only be conjugated in the Cat form. These are called perfect verbs. They indiCate actions or states of being which only Cats experience. They follow the Cat form of Class One and Two verbs.

prip(b4) — grant, bestow, dispense, give, vouchsafe

mow prip(b4) **ma`** — you may bring food

mRaow pirp(c4) (lit. 'I grant that you may offer food')[17]

These verbs are indiCated in the vocabulary with the notation (C) after the BNTP indicator.

6 COMPREHENSION EXERCISE

m'mow(a1) **mRaow**(a3) **'aa**(c7) **Row**(a4) **row**(a1). **maowr**(a2) **'aa pwah**(f 7) **praow**(c4). **mRaow**(b3) **mow**(a1) **bRuh**(b4). **mew**(d4) **mow**(a1) **pra mraow**(b4) **uh mew**(a4) **mow pra bRRow**(a1) **uh bRRow**(b4).

---

[17] Note the difference between the perfect verb **prip**(b4) – to bestow, grant or vouchsafe, and the defective verb **pirp**(c4) – to give or offer, make an offering

7 PRACTICE EXERCISES

1   'Aa has played a good joke. BRRow laughed.
2   I (nC) have put the tuna in your (C) bowl.
3   I (nC) have cleaned your bowl.
4   Last night the Cat played a trick and we (nC) laughed.
5   In the morning, the Cat likes to eat a titbit.

8 TEST FOR PROGRESS

The story of BRRow and 'Aa, presented at the beginning of the chapter, is much loved by Cats. Ask your Cat to listen while you read it to her. Monitor the Cat's response. If she laughs,[18] congratulations! You have been studying well.

The Cat may offer some corrections in your pronunciation. Listen carefully.

If the Cat does not laugh, or if she loses attention and walks away before the story is finished, you are not ready to proceed beyond this chapter. Go over the sections on tonality again.

---

[18] Remember that the Cat laugh is **bRRow**(d1)!

Chapter Four

The Flattery Voice
Questions
Attributes
The plural
Definite and indefinite

maow(d4)	Song[1]
mow 'Rowow(d2)	you (are) pretty
mow wah(d1)	you (are) handsome
rrow mboh	big whiskers
b'row uh b'row b'row(d1)	unnumbered hairs[2]
mbruh ma`row(b3)	a fine coat
broh meow(d4)	discerning eye
mir meow	sharp claw
rowb(b6)	(the parts adjacent to) the tail
rro(d4)	clean
rir(d4)	(you are worthy of) music
mbo(d3)	(you are worthy of the) name
rir	music
mrruh	name
uhmeuh	nine
mow(d4) **mbruuh**(d1)	Mow is pleased (with you)

VOCABULARY

^ow(f4)(nC)	trousers, jeans, skin, clothes	**m'aaw**(b4)(C)	to fight (nobly), to engage in battle
arp(b4, c4)	to run, scurry	**meow**(d1)	today
b'row(d1)	hair	**meow**(d4)	good, sharp, clear
b'row uh b'row	'hairs of', i.e. many, numerous, uncountable	**mir**(d1)	claw, claws
brap(b4, c4)	to eat	**mrrew**(f 7)	name(nC)
broh(a4)	eye	**mrruh**(d3)	name (C)
brroh(d4)	shadow	**rir**(d4)	music
maow(d4)	song	**rowb**(d1)	tail
maowro(b4, c4)	to sing	**Row^**(b1)	lap, knee
mbruuh(a1, d1)[3]	to be pleased with, to approve	**rro**(d4)	cleanliness
		waa`(c4)(nC)	to scrap, to fight
		wah(d1)	handsome

[1] This is a song Cats tend to sing when sitting in bright sunlight, having cleaned themselves after a good meal. In modern times it has become quite permissible for a human to sing the song to a Cat.

[2] lit, 'hairs of' hair. See Chapter Seven.

[3] See Chapter Seven, Class Three verbs.

1 THE FLATTERY VOICE

There is no exact equivalent of the Flattery Voice in any European language. This is a form of the verb that denotes a degree of certainty higher than that expressed in the indiCative mood. The indiCative is used in statements of fact, such as, 'She *is* irritated', and the subjunctive in statements of doubt or possibility, such as, 'I think that she *may* be musical.' The Flattery Voice might be expressed by the statement, 'It is certain that she is offended' or 'What a fine voice she has!'

The Flattery Voice is formed by elongating the vowel sound of adjectives. Sometimes the word order may be changed. Verbs of state of being may be omitted.

mow row 'Rowow	–	you are beautiful (indiCative)
mow 'Row<u>ow</u>	–	you are so beautiful; how beautiful you are!

WHEN TO USE THE FLATTERY VOICE

a. A Cat may indiCate willingness to hear the Flattery Voice in one of three ways:

1   by arching the back invitingly.
2   by pressing the head firmly against some part of a human's body.
3   by repeating **rrup**(a1)[4] one or several times.

However, the Flattery Voice needs no invitation. Many Cats now consider a statement in the Flattery Voice a sufficient introduction from a human, and in such cases, it would have the same weight as the more traditional offer of food, **mRaow,** outlined in Chapter Two.[5]

In situations where you have reason to believe that a Cat may be hungry, however, you should retain the traditional form of greeting.[6]

b. A communiCation in the Flattery Voice must always precede and follow any discussion of a Cat other than the one with whom you are speaking. This is called the bracket or parenthesis, and the effect is exactly what that

---

[4]   **rrup** has no English equivalent. It has been called the 'Invitation to Intimacy'. You should always make a communiCation in the Flattery Voice when you hear this word.

[5]   This fact may be explained by the fact that, like humans, Cats tend to be better fed now than in the past, and therefore pleasing descriptions of the Cat are quite as welcome as food.

[6]   You may be surprised to hear Cats use the Flattery Voice among themselves in situations where it is clear compliment is not intended. Between equals, the Flattery Voice is called the Descriptive Voice, and may also be used to express disapproval. You should never under any circumstances attempt to use it in this fashion. *Humans should not express, or indeed feel, disapproval of Cats.* It is grammatically unsound. See Chapter Nine, Apology.

term indiCates: to mark the communiCation as secondary to the main topic.[7]

1 **mow 'R<u>ow</u>ow meow** – my, you're looking lovely today!
2 **mow Lorna nrow?** – Lorna Cat not around?
3 **uh w<u>a</u>h ma`row** – and you have an extremely
   w<u>a</u>h mow row(b4)! handsome coat!

2 QUESTIONS

Direct questions are rare in Cat; they are considered rude.[8] Information is elicited in other ways.

a. Statement

A Cat whose dinner is late will not, unless extremely inconvenienced, ask, 'Where is my dinner?' Instead,

m'mow m'ow(d1) nrow – my dinner is not in my dish
  'aa Row
mupRup m'mow m'ow pirp – you must bring my dinner[9]

b. Challenge

Where information rather than action is desired, the Challenge form – stating something as fact and waiting to be challenged – is used. Non-Cats may use the Challenge form of question in certain circumstances.

mow merowwap – are you hungry? (lit. you (Cat) are hungry)

The verb **bRuh**(b4) 'desire, wish' may be used in the challenge form:

---

[7] The rules for conducting historical discussions are more complex than this, and beyond the scope of this work – and your abilities at this level. Beware!

[8] Since there is so much misinformation at present about it, a word must be said here about **'arra**. This is the 'true' question form. The word **'arra**(a7), placed immediately before any sentence, takes the place of the English words Who, What, Where, When, Why, depending on the context.

    'arra row(f 7)? – What is it?
    'arra ma` row? – Who are you (nC)?

However, as a number of syntactical louts and fools have discovered, **'arra** may also be used as a general term of abuse. Thus, *in certain circumstances,* the questions above are not so much an expression of interest as a term of opprobrium, perhaps better translated respectively as, 'What the bleep is this?' and 'Who the devil are you?'

    For this reason *you should make no attempt to use the true question form until you have attained a high degree of fluency in Cat.* Any use of this term to enquire into a Cat's likes, dislikes or activities, for example, would be a grave offence. (See Chapter Nine, Apology.) Use the 'challenge' form for questioning.

[9] In extreme cases, this may be spoken in the Offended Voice. See Chapter Seven.

mow bRuh(b4) **birr**(b5)	– would you (C) like some milk? (lit. you would like milk)
mow bRuh ma` birr(b1) **bra**	– shall I fetch you a cushion? (you would like me to fetch a cushion)

3 ATTRIBUTES

mow ruh(a7) **rrow** – the Cat's whiskers

a. It probably struck you, during the discussion of possessives in Chapter Three, that without a non-Cat possessive, you have no way to indiCate such things as 'the dog's tail', 'my (nC) knee' and the like.

Cat does not consider that *attributes* are in a possessed relationship with the creature they define. This is called the 'attributive' relationship. The pronoun or noun is followed by the word **ruh** (a7, c7) and then by the attribute.[10]

mow(a1) **maow**(b4) **uh** **prruh**(a1) **'aa ma`**(f 7) **ruh**(c7) **Row^**(b1)	– are you going to come and sit on my (nC) lap? (lit. the Cat Presence is coming and sitting on me as defined by lap)
maaa` mow(a1) **ruh**(a7) **rowb!**	– get off my (C) tail!

b. *In extremis*, the attribute construction may be used to indiCate non-Cat possession, but it must be stressed that no Cat will tolerate repeated use of this essentially ungrammatical construct.[11]

b'row uh b'row 'aa ma` ruh **^ow**(a4) **row. mow pra prruh** **'aa ^ow**	– There are hairs all over my trousers. Have you been taking your ease on them?[12]

---

[10] The opposite construction is also common. **ma` ruh Row^** – 'me as defined by lap'; **Row^ ruh ma`** – 'lap as an attribute of me'.

[11] Always think twice before using any non-Cat possessive. Ask yourself if it is really a necessary communiCation *from the Cat's point of view*. In the writer's opinion, the statement here is totally unnecessary. Both you and the Cat know how the hairs got on your trousers. Furthermore, the whole thing fails in its intent (being, of course, to induce guilt in the Cat) since to a Cat the leaving of hairs on anything constitutes a blessing. For this reason the Cat (who does not like to have her generosity drawn attention to, and certainly will not stand being thanked) will ignore the whole communiCation.

[12] Lit. 'you have taken your ease on my trousers'. Remember never to use the **'arra** form of question under any circumstances. **'arra mow prruh 'aa ma` ruh ^ow**, for example, would not translate simply, 'Have you been lying on my trousers?' but something like, 'Have you been defeCating hair all over my bleeping trousers, dingbat?' and most Cats would find this offensive. It is doubtful if even a Ninth Level apology would be effective after such a grammatical solecism. (See Chapter Nine, Apology.).

4 THE PLURAL

a. Plural nouns [13]

1. Two repetitions of a noun indiCate the number two or simply the idea of plurality.

mow pra brap prrew prrew   –   I ate (a brace of) mice

2. Two repetitions joined by **uh** ('and') indiCate 'many'.

mow brap prrew uh prrew   –   I eat a lot of mice

3. An undefined plural is served by the singular.

awa(f 7) **morh**(c4)   –   the dog bites, or dogs bite

b. Plural nouns with Class One verbs

1. Two singular subjects, when not mixed, will normally take one plural verb.

mow uh mow Maureen   –   are you(C) and Maureen
   m`ma` bRRow(a1)   Cat laughing at me?

2. Cat and non-Cat may never be served by the same Class One verb.[14]

mow bRRow(a1) **uh ma`**   –   you(C) and I(nC) are
   bRRow(f 7) –   laughing.

c. Plural nouns with Class Two verbs

1. Again, where two singular subjects are unmixed, they share a verb.

mow uh mow Blacky bRuh(b4)   –   Blacky and I would like a
   mRRah   snack

2. Because Class Two verbs indiCate action taken, the non-Cat form of the verb may be omitted where a Cat verb already conveys the sense. The non-Cat pronoun does not precede the Cat verb.

mow arp(b4) **uh prrew**   –   you (C) and the mouse are running

NOTE: The *Cat* form of the verb may never be omitted. *No Cat subject may ever be served by a non-Cat verb.*

---

[13] For nouns defined by numbers, see Chapter Seven, Numbers.

[14] Because they indiCate state of being. It may be true, as Antichat has pointed out, that 'il y a deux *niveaux* d'état d'éxistence, et certainement l'état d'éxistence de chat est plus élevé que celui de non-chat', but such speculation is unnecessary for the elucidation of what is, after all, a simple point of grammar.

d. Perfect Verbs with Defective Verbs

A defective verb may not be omitted in conjunction with a perfect verb.

mow m'aaw(b4) uh awa(f 7)   –   the Cat and dog are fighting[15]
  waa`(c4)

e. Plural adjectives

Adjectives do not agree in number with nouns.

mir(d1) meow   –   sharp claw
mir mir meow   –   sharp claws

The plural noun may bracket the adjective modifier.

mrruh mowruh mrruh   –   noble names

5 DEFINITE AND INDEFINITE

There are no articles equivalent to the English 'the' and 'a'.

mow broh prrew   –   I (C) see *a* mouse
mow broh prrew   –   I (C) see *the* mouse

6 COMPREHENSION EXERCISE

'Rowow(d2) mow 'Rowow 'Rowow. mow broh(a4) meow(d4) row(b4) uh prrew pra broh(b4). prrew ruh rowb irr irr (pra) row(a1)? irr irr row(a1).

7 PRACTICE EXERCISES

1.   I (C) see hundreds (lit. 'hairs of') of birds.
2.   Your (C) tail is in the milk.
3.   You (C) are taking a nap on your cushion.
4.   My (C) eye is very sharp.
5.   At night you (C) eat your dinner, and in the morning you have your titbits.
6.   Did you (C) eat the dog's food? (lit. You ate the not your food–dog. Remember not to use the **'arra** form!)

---

[15] Lit. 'the Cat is engaged in noble battle and a dog is scrapping pitifully', but such purely grammatical distinctions should, at this level of study, be ignored.

8 FIELD TEST

Approach a strange Cat (one you have not tried to speak to before).[16] After an exchange of greetings, make a favourable comment about its appearance, intelligence, singing voice or disposition, being sure to use the Flattery Voice. If the Cat responds, make another. Try to achieve a position where you retain the Cat's attention for five Flattery Voice observations. (Be imaginative! Nothing bores a Cat so fast as the same old 'what fine whiskers you have!' and the like, day after day.)

Do not move on to Chapter Five until this has been achieved.

[16] It is only common sense, but some students do need to be told, not to approach a Cat who is engaged on business. A Cat studying birds, contemplating her name, or involved in purity ritual, for example, will have no time for a human communiCation, however flattering. If a Cat responds to your Flattery Voice communiCation with an Offended, or even Bored Blink, *do not persist*. 'Humans do not understand that a Cat who in human terms appears inactive may yet be too busy to speak to them' (Johnny, 3.12.95; 2:15). In this, Cats are not unlike writers.

Chapter Five

Imperative
The future tense
Direct and indirect objects
Expressions of time
Names

'Rowowmiuh   The Artist

mew(d4). mow 'aa a`bRah row. mow ar(a1) truh a`bRah ruh(b2) mir(d1). mow me`a(a1) truh mir 'aa trrow(b1). mow meuh`a b'row uh b'row maor(a5) mew(b4). 'Rowow 'Rowow row. ma` maow(c4). ma`braa`(f 7). mow m`Row^(b1) ruh ma` prruh(b4). mow miaow: *maaa` mow Rup*(c4). ma` meuh`a broh mow pra mew(b4). ma`aaa`: *mow pra truh a`bRah ruh maor*(d1). *'Rowow row 'Rowow. wah uh wah a`bRah. RRow me`a maor nrow.* ma` aaa`(c4) brroh(d1) mew(d4) m`mew(a4).

Night. The Cat is in the bathroom. She is going to decorate the bathroom with her claws. First, she sharpens her claws on the curtains. Then she sculpts many yards of paper. It is very beautiful. The human comes in and sits down. The Cat reclines on its lap. 'Stroke me,' says the Cat. Meanwhile, the human sees what the Cat has sculpted. 'Cat,' says the human, 'you have decorated the bathroom with artist's paper. How beautiful it is! What a pity there is not more of it.' The human squeaks admiringly for a long time.

VOCABULARY

a`bRah(b1)	bathroom	**mew**(d4) **m`mew**(a4)	for a long time, 'from night till morning'
aaa`(c4)(nC)	to squeak, say		
ar(a1)	intention		
braa`(f 7)(nC)	to sit	**mrrew**(f 7)	name(nC)
brroh(a1)	admiringly, in admiration	**mrruh**(d3)	name(C)
		pra^(b7)	sofa, firm claw sharpener
m`	to, for, at, from, off, etc.	**prruh**(b4)(C)	to rest, recline, to grace, to be at ease
maor(d1)	paper, toilet/artist's paper	**Row^**(b1)	lap, knee
maow(b4, c4)	to come, walk, move forward	**ruh**(b2)	with, by means of
		Rup(c4)(nC)	to stroke, worship through caress
me`a	first; now		
meuh`a	second; then; afterwards; meanwhile; while	**trrow**(b1)	curtains, ladder, soft claw sharpener
		truh(b4, c4)	to stir, mix, prepare; improve, adjust, knead, decorate; scratch; sharpen
mew(b4)(C)	decorate, rearrange, sculpt; pull		

54

1 THE IMPERATIVE

a. The imperative is formed by elongating the vowel of the pronoun **ma`** 'you(nC)'. The extended pronoun retains its BNTS[1] (f 7).

> **maaa` pirp m'mow**(a1) **maowr**(a4)   –   give me some salmon
> **maaa` Rup**(c4) **mow ruh ma`row**   –   stroke my fur

b. The extended pronoun also stands alone. It is a general instruction to cease some activity unpleasing to the Cat.

> **maaa`**   –   cut it out!

c. There is no form of imperative for non-Cat use.[2] Humans may use their own language, such as English, to give an order to a Cat, but such commands are actually outside the comprehension area of most Cats.[3]

2 THE FUTURE TENSE

The future tense, called by Cats 'the intention indiCator', is formed by inserting the future particle **ar** (a1, f 7) before the verb.

> **mow a`bRah ar**(a1) **truh**   –   the Cat is going to decorate the bathroom
> **ma` m`mow ar**(f 7) **bra birr birr**   –   I (nC) will fetch you (some) cream

NOTE: Because it expresses *intention*, in certain situations it is inappropriate for humans to use the future tense. Do not use this construction to express such thoughts as, 'I'm going to stroke you now,' since this does not depend upon your intention but the Cat's.

> **mow ar prip m`ma` mow Rup**   –   will you allow me to stroke you?

3 DIRECT AND INDIRECT OBJECTS

A direct object is someone or something that directly receives the action of the verb. An indirect object receives the action only indirectly. In the sentence, 'Rufus bit Fitz on the back leg', *Fitz* is the *direct object* of the verb *bit*, while *the back leg* is the *indirect object* governed by the preposition *on*.

---

[1] Begin Note–Tonal Shape.
[2] A form between Cats is in wide use, but there is no need for humans to know it. Any attempt on your part to use an imperative to a Cat would be a serious grammatical error. See Chapter 9, Apology.
[3] And therefore, genuinely not heard. Antichat's views on this subject (expressed in a recent tabloid newspaper article) are both erroneous and invidious.

a. There is no direct object marker. In ordinary statements direct objects follow the verb.

> **mow pra morh**(b4) **mow Fitz** – I bit Fitz

Where the statement is emphatic, such as when an order is given or there is firm intent, the direct object may precede the action verb. It never precedes the imperative.

> **mupRup maor bra** – you must fetch more artist's paper
> **ma` birr ar bra** *or*
> **ma` ar bra birr** – I will bring milk[4]

b. Indirect objects are signified by the preposition **m`** preceding the noun or pronoun.[5] It may mean 'to, for, at' or any similar preposition in English. It always adopts the Begin Note of the word it precedes. Indirect objects generally precede the verb.

> **mow m`ma` ruh Row^ prruh**(b4) – the Cat reclines on the
> human's lap
> **maaa` truh**(c4) **m`mow**(a1) – stir (it) for me

c. It is not always easy to know whether an object is direct or indirect in Cat, and even fluent speakers often make mistakes. There is no rule, except to learn as you go. Generally speaking no apology is required for a mistake of this type.

> **mow pra morh mow Fitz ruh aw** – You bit Fitz on the paw *or*
> you bit Fitz's paw

4 EXPRESSIONS OF TIME

a. Expressions of time may stand alone.

> **mew**(d4) – (it was) night(time)
> **mew**(d4) **m`mew** – (it went on for) a long time
> (lit. 'from night till morning')

b. Where they form part of a longer sentence, they generally follow the subject.

> **mow me`a truh mir** – first, the Cat sharpens her claws

---

[4] The former use is preferred because it puts the human in a laudable light. The Cat expression meaning 'pie in the sky' is **birrmuhRRownpirpawama`**, lit. 'an offer of milk that does not precede the verb'.

[5] Do not confuse **m`** (indirect object marker) with **m'** the possessive particle.

5 NAMES

Names are an extremely important area of Cat culture. There is, however, a high degree of secrecy surrounding the subject. That there is some actual function attached to names now seems clear, but what that function might be remains a mystery.

Some Cats may have more names than others, but if so, the reasons for this are unknown.[6] It seems possible that what humans call the Ordinary and Particular names[7] have both been invented solely for use by humans, although Cats do apparently sometimes use the Particular name among themselves. It is best not to engage in much discussion of names with any Cat you do not know extremely well. This text will restrict itself to a few forms for enquiring as to name.

a. Between Cats

Cats, much more than humans, require to know other Cats' names. It now seems certain that every Cat has at least some names beyond the Ordinary and Particular, and that these may be used only according to rigid rules regarding the relationship and level of intimacy subsisting between Cats. The methods of ascertaining the various names among Cats are apparently complex. Humans will rarely overhear these quasi-sacred formulae, and will never use them.

Cats never use, or enquire into, the Ordinary name among themselves. It is entirely for use with humans. However, some Cats nowadays do enquire as to another Cat's Particular name in the presence of humans, and for interest's sake, this form is given here.

mowuh ruh[8] **mrruh**	— what is your Particular name?
mow(d4) **ruh rowb**(d1)	(lit. your name (is) God's tailtip)[9]

---

[6] The ancient world, in particular the Egyptian priests, had a clearer understanding of these matters. See Part Four, EINSTEIN'S CAT.

[7] See Eliot, *The Naming of Cats*, op. cit., p.1ff. Eliot listed three levels of name ('the name that the family use daily', the 'name that's particular . . . that's more dignified', and 'the name that no human research can discover'). Even if higher levels are proved to exist, his theory of the three tiers of name was groundbreaking, and must be considered correct in essentials. It is well worth study.

[8] Note that names are considered **attributes**.

[9] It has been suggested (Rechter, 'Namen und 'Challenge' – neun frage', *KS*, Spring, 1991, pp. 112–38) that there is a long train of such questions, ending in the request to know the Cat's Most Secret Name. According to this theory, the final (ninth) question is 'Your name is Divinity's Ninth Sensor.' It is this phrase that is said to have given rise to the term 'Cat's whiskers' in English, since the Ninth Sensor is also called The Whisker. This is very speculative.

b. Between Cat and Human

1. The formula for a human to ask a Cat's Ordinary name is new, and is a back-formation from the above formula. Please remember the warning in Chapter One regarding the addressing of Cats. It would be an offence to ask a Cat who has not first addressed you what her name is.

mow(a1) **ruh mrruh mow**(d4)	– what is your Ordinary name?
ruh aw(d1)	(lit. your name (is) God's paw)

Under no circumstances should you ever ask a Cat's Particular name. A Cat may volunteer this information, but any enquiry would be an offence. *It is for a Cat to initiate any change in the level of intimacy between Cat and human.*

2. Cats rarely ask humans their names. It is the highest form of compliment. The formula used is as follows:

ma` ruh mrrew(f 7) **'aa mow**	– your name (falls) within
ruh brroh	God's shadow

The response to this is simply to state your name.[10]

NAMES AND INSULT

In a particularly bad mood, Cats sometimes use the form **`arra ma` ruh mrrew row?** (What the bleeping cheapside is your name?) This is meant as an insult. The best recourse is to pretend not to have heard. *Do not* respond to this question with your name. If you should happen to overhear one Cat put this question to another Cat, leave the vicinity if at all possible.

6 COMPREHENSION EXERCISE

mow m'ma` ruh**(c7) **Row^**(b1) **prruh**(b4). **mow a`bRah pra(c7) **truh. mow me`a m`ma` ruh Row^ truh**(b4). **ma` meuh`a m`mow ruh ma`row Rup**(c4). **mow ar mRRow**(b4).

7 PRACTICE EXERCISES

1. You (C) have decorated the bathroom. It is pretty.
2. You (C) were kneading the curtains.
3. Stroke me while I (C) take my ease on your lap.
4. The Cat is going to sculpt the toilet (artist's) paper.
5. The Cat is gracing the sofa with her presence.

---

[10] The old form of genuflection by stroking the tailtip as you speak your name is now considered very *passé*. Cats are extremely democratic and most prefer to let such old usages slide. However, if you should make the mistake of adopting the old form, and a Cat expresses disapproval, apology would be inappropriate.

8 REVIEW – PICK OUT THE ERRORS

Read the section below, picking out the grammatical errors and social solecisms. Then check your answers against the ones given below.

NOTE: **Do not read this section to your Cat.**

> *Georgina, a Cat, and Marilyn, a human, have never met before. Georgina is sitting on Marilyn's garden wall, watching a butterfly. The butterfly leaves, whereupon Georgina notices Marilyn, who is standing quietly nearby.*
>
> | MOW: | **mow**(a1). |
> | MA`: | **mow.*** |
>
> *Georgina presses her head against Marilyn's arm.*
>
> | MOW: | **rrup.** |
> | MA`: | **mow merowwap?**** |
> | MOW: | **moh.** |
> | MA`: | **'arra m'mow mrrew row?***** |
>
> *Georgina involuntarily claws Marilyn, taking care to spoil her new cashmere sweater.*

ANSWERS

* Although grammatically **mow** is an acceptable response to the greeting **mow**, in practice, where a human meets a Cat for the first time, **ma`** is more precise. It indiCates a general character of willingness to be of service to the Cat, and thus promotes good inter-species relations.

**Although technically no offer of food is taken amiss, Marilyn should not have ignored Georgina's Invitation to Intimacy. The correct response is with a communiCation in the Flattery Voice. When two or three such comments have been accepted, time enough to go on to the offer of food.

***This is an extreme grammatical, syntactical and social solecism. Did you recognise the triple error? Marilyn's first error is social – she has instigated a discussion of names before Georgina has indiCated any interest in the subject. Her second error is syntactical – she has used **mrrew**, which is restricted to non-Cat names. Her third error is by far the most serious: she uses the question form **'arra**. This error is rendered even more egregious because it pertains to a Cat's name. Of course it is unlikely that any Cat, however provoked, would react in the manner stated. It is put here to make you aware of the enormity of the insult in human terms. Marilyn will probably be under an embargo[11] by Cats for some time.

---

[11] An embargo of this type is not now and never has been called a 'Catwa'. This is a joke that has gone far enough.

Chapter Six

Colour Names
Here and there
Here is, there is
This and that
Comparison
Attention

mowmew

The Kittens

mow Minou 'aa 'iaou(a4) prruh(b4). mow m`mowmew(d2) m'ow(b2) miaow.

Minou is lying in her basket. She speaks softly to her kittens.

ma` broh brroh m`mowmew. mia'. bRuh(c4) Rup mowmew.[1] mow mowruh mbruuh.

The human is admiring the kittens. Its attention is pleasant. It wants to stroke the kittens. Minou graciously grants permission.

ma` mowmew brrow(d1) morih(c4). mowmew brrow miaow: *mew*(d4).

The human picks up the kitten of white coat with six black hairs on his occiput. 'Mew,' says the kitten.[2]

aaa`: *mowmew brrow mowruh*(d4) *row!* mowmew brrow Rup(c4). mowmew brrow moreh(c4). mowmew friuh(d2) morih.

'He is adorable,' says the human. It strokes the white kitten[3] and puts it down. It picks up the black kitten with white nose, breast and three paws, excluding the right forepaw.

aaa`: *nr'mow mowmew mboh mboh mowmew brroh row.*

'This kitten is bigger than the white one.'

mow maow miaow: *ow ow nmbruh.*

Minou gently warns,[4] 'Comparisons are invidious.'

aaa` preh'(c1): *mowmew 'Rowow row 'Rowow 'Rowow. mowmew 'Rowow ruh mow*(d4).

'They are all most beautiful,' says the human hastily. 'Each is as beautiful as Mow.'[5]

---

[1] Alert students will wonder why the direct object here does not precede the verb, since the intention must of course be very high. This is because it is inappropriate for the human to have a firm intention to stroke the kittens before the Cat has given permission.

[2] Lit. 'The kitten speaks the Sacred Word.' By tradition, all kittens speak a mysterious sacred word which adult Cats can neither speak nor understand. It is assumed that this sound is the Central Note of the Universe.

[3] Through considerations of space, the full descriptions of Cat coat colours are not repeated.

[4] Lit. 'speaks in Second Maow'. See Chapter Eight.

[5] A common expression used of kittens when speaking to the Mother Cat.

VOCABULARY

'aiou(a4)	bed; basket; washtub; drawer	**merah**(b4)	house
^ra`(b1)	toy	**moreh**(c4)(nC)	to put down
breh(b2)	tree	**morih**(c4)(nC)	to pick up
breh(c2)	wall	**m'ow**(b2)	softly, gently
brrow(d1)	white with blue eyes, six black hairs on the occiput	**mow**(b3)	good
		mowmew(d2)	kitten, kittens
bru(d2)	white, no markings	**mowruh**(d3)	adorable, worthy of adoration/ worship
frah(d4)	black, no markings		
friuh(d2)	black with white nose, breast and three paws, the right fore black	**mrah**(d1)	cream with dark nose, paws and tailtip
		mrah(d2)	grey, no markings
		mrah(d4)	tabby, no white
irr(a5)	delicious	**mruh**(d4)	ginger, no white
maaa(a4)	floor	**nr'mow**(a1)	there
maow(a7) **miaow**(b4)	to warn gently	**preh**(c1)	quickly
		pwah(a1, f 7)	to dislike, disdain
mboh(c5)	big	**r'mow**(a1)	here

1 COLOUR NAMES

Cat is very rich in colour descriptive words. Cats do not recognise anything resembling what humans call 'breed' among Cats. No generic term for 'Siamese', 'Tabby', 'Burmese', etc., exists in the language. Instead, there are almost as many words to describe types of fur colouring as there are Cats.

For example, there are at least four words to describe identically striped tabbies according to how wide the central stripe running along the spine is, and many different terms for white Cats with various single and multiple markings.

It is virtually impossible for a human being to learn all these various descriptive words, particularly as some of the distinguishing characteristics are not visible to the human apparatus.[6] This chapter gives you several basic colour terms, and you may wish, by a challenge question, to use the term closest to your own Cat to determine the correct word.

[6] It is complete nonsense to imagine, as some scientists do, that Cats do not perceive colour. In fact, Cats have a more sensitive eye than humans. In addition to the 'human' spectrum, Cats perceive colours in a spectrum that (in allegorical terms) runs at 90 degrees to it.

If your Cat is ginger, for example, the question,

mow mruh(d4) **row** – are you a ginger Cat (without white markings)?

may elicit some such response as

mow ufrah(d1) **row** – I have orange and ochre intermingled stripes, white forepaws, variegated hindpaws, a broad white breast patch running to a point between the forelegs; the tip of the tail deep ochre.

Once a Cat has imparted its Colour Name to you, be sure to learn it. It is an offence to use a wrong Colour Name twice (see Chapter Nine).[7]

2 HERE AND THERE

By now you should have begun to appreciate that the worldview of Cats is fundamentally different from our own. This difference appears again when we search for a way of expressing the English concepts 'here' and 'there'. In English, generally, when we say 'here', we mean 'close to me (the speaker) or to the position in space which I am inhabiting.' 'There' usually means 'far from me (the speaker) or the space I am inhabiting, in a particular direction.'

In Cat, **r'mow** (a1) and **nr'mow** (a1) – 'here' and 'there', are always *relative to the position of the Cat*, regardless of who is speaking. If you remember that the literal translation of these terms is 'in Cat's presence' and 'not in Cat's presence', you will find it easier to keep the distinctions in mind.

a. When a Cat is speaking, the terms are straightforward.

mRaow r'mow nrow(a1) – (my) food is not here (i.e. not near me(C))

maaa` nr'mow moreh(c4) – put it there

b. When a human is speaking

1. **When Cat and human are in close proximity**, as for example, when your knee is occupied by a Cat, 'here' for you will naturally be **r'mow**, since you yourself are in the Cat's presence. It follows that anything not close to you, 'there', is also 'not in the Cat's presence', **nr'mow**.

ma` r'mow row – I (nC) am here (with you) [8]

---

7 Much as with humans, Colour Names may be used between Cats as terms of abuse. This involves altering the BNTP of the Colour Name. Therefore be very careful about accepting from one Cat a Colour Name for another Cat. Get your information straight from the Cat's tongue.

8 There are strong overtones to this apparently simple statement that tend to make it pleasing

2. **When the human and Cat are not in close proximity,** often a human speaker of Cat may simply *reverse* these words. Thus, 'here' will generally mean 'not in Cat presence', **nr'mow**, since what is close to you will not be close to the Cat, and 'there' will be 'in Cat presence', **r'mow**, if it is close to the Cat. If you are speaking of an object or place not close to you *and* not close to the Cat you are addressing, you would naturally use the form **nr'mow**, 'not in Cat's presence'.

c. 'There' has greater force in English than **nr'mow**. Most things that are **nr'mow** are of no interest to a Cat, and indeed the word is often used to express a Cat's lack of interest in something.[9] If you were to say to a Cat **mRaow**(b3) **row**(a1) **nr'mow**(a1), '(Your) food is there', the word **nr'mow** will have much the same force and meaning as does 'there' in the English sentence. However, the sentence, 'The dog is there', **awa row nr'mow**, does not carry the meaning, as it does in English, The dog is in a specific, indiCated place.' It would mean simply, 'The dog is of no interest.'

3 HERE IS, HERE ARE

'Here is' in English is relatively closely translated by the Cat **ma` pirp r'mow**, 'I offer into Cat's presence.'

> **birr pirp r'mow** — here is your milk

This also serves for plural constructions.

> **mRRah mRRah pirp r'mow** — here are a few titbits

Where the meaning is not emphatic, the verb **row** is used.

> **Johnny row**(a1) — here's Johnny (lit. 'it's Johnny')

4 THERE IS, THERE ARE

Where the meaning is not emphatic, the verb **row** is used.

> **mowmew 'aa aiou**(a4) **row** — there are kittens in the basket

Where the meaning is emphatic, the construction is more difficult. For ordinary conversational purposes it is best to avoid this construction. Remember that anything not close to a Cat is rarely of interest unless it is making sounds or movement which will announce its own presence.

For example, **marr**(a5) **nr'mow**(a1) **row**, ostensibly 'There's a bird', may be spoken by a Cat in certain situations, but the expression will then carry

---

to Cats. Literally, 'the non-Cat is in the presence of Cat', it communiCates a sense of being honoured and a gratitude almost epiphany that are not obvious in the English.
[9] cf. the English 'neither here nor there'.

overtones of intent as well as interest. It would be inappropriate for you ever to announce the presence of a bird at a distance, since any Cat's powers of perception in such matters far surpass your own, and you would be guilty of the peculiarly human sin, roundly disliked by Cats, called ^^^ow(f7) 'redundancy' or 'unnecessariness'.[10] See Chapter Nine, Apology.

5 THIS AND THAT

The English 'this' and 'that' are expressed by **r'mow** and **nr'mow**, 'here' and 'there'.

mowmew nr'mow 'Rowow row –	this kitten (i.e. the one not near you the Cat) is beautiful

6 COMPARISON

Cats consider comparison invidious. Avoid comparing one Cat with another. A simple statement such as **mow 'Rowow row** – 'You are pretty' will always be sufficient; there is no need whatsoever to attempt any such construction as, for example, 'You are the most beautiful Cat in the world.' Any mention of a Cat not present to one who is is somewhat insulting (see Chapter Four). To mention *all the other Cats in the world* would deeply offend any normally sensitive Cat. (See Chapter Nine, Apology.)

a. The Repetitious or Self-defined Comparative

Of course, you will frequently want to express the thought that a particular Cat is, as it were, 'more than pretty'. This is achieved by *intensifying*, that is, through the means of doubling or bracketing of adjectives described in Chapter Two.

'Rowow mow 'Rowow	– more than pretty Cat
mow(b3) **maow**(d4) **mow**(b3)	– a better song

b. The Self-Defined Superlative

A triple repetition of the adjective is the equivalent of the English superlative[11] and as a construction is generally very welcome to most Cats.

'Rowow mow 'Rowow	– you are the prettiest Cat! *or* you are
'Rowow row	as pretty as pretty can be[12]

NOTE: It is quite permissible to combine the repetitious comparative or superlative with the Flattery Voice.

---

[10] In the case of an old or infirm Cat, the insult of pointing out, for example, a bird whose presence the Cat has not detected should be avoided at all costs.

[11] cf. the archaic English 'thrice-pretty Cat'.

[12] Not 'as pretty as a Cat can be', since by definition there is no limit to how pretty – or anything else – a Cat can be.

mow 'R<u>ow</u>ow row 'R<u>ow</u>ow   –   you certainly are one supremely
   'R<u>ow</u>ow   beautiful Cat

c. 'True' Comparative and Superlative

These forms are used rarely, and only in a purely descriptive and above all non-judgemental way, with reference to inanimate objects. *All judgemental comparisons should be left to Cats.*

POSITIVE	COMPARATIVE	SUPERLATIVE
adjective	**ow**(a7) + adjective	**ow**(a7) **ow**(a7) + adjective
big	bigger	biggest
mboh (c5)	**ow mboh**	**ow ow mboh**

NOTE: The most common use of the true comparative and superlative among Cats is for insult. As the author can attest from personal experience, even a simple statement such as

mow ruh ma`row ow frah(d4)   –   your coat is darker than Blacky's
   row Blacky

may be taken as a grave insult. Although the point is not yet quite clear, it seems that, when directed at sentient individuals, **ow** may have a pejorative connotation. It is safer to use the repetitious comparative.

breh(b4) **mboh mboh row**   –   the tree is bigger than the house
   merah(b4)

7 A NOTE ON ATTENTION

Cats divide attention into Positive or Pleasant Attention, **mia**'(d4), and Negative or Uncomfortable Attention, **pra**'(f 7). Both types of attention are within the Cat visibility range, occurring along the sensation/colour spectrum – **mrrowa**(d1) – which runs perpendicularly to our spectrum. This spectrum extends beyond the visual into other senses. (As indeed do the extremes of our spectrum, the flavour/colour/sensation spectrum – **mrroh**(d1): beyond ultra violet is a sweetish boney flavour, for example; beyond infra red there is a light stroking sensation.) In the **mrrowa** spectrum, Positive Attention has what has variously been translated as a 'warm' or 'musical' colour/tone. Negative Attention has an unpleasantly scratchy or buzzing colour.

It is not at all easy for humans to control the nature of their attention. A too-eager human who feels entirely positive feelings towards a Cat is nevertheless capable of extending highly uncomfortable Negative Attention. This is particularly true of children.

The easiest way of getting the feel of Positive Attention is to monitor yourself when reading a *reasonably interesting* newspaper article. Cats trying to train humans will often come and sit in this attention, which is extremely pleasant. This is the colour of attention Cats like best. The crunkle of newsprint as the Cat reclines on it adds an attractive note to the colour melody.

8 COMPREHENSION EXERCISE

mow bru(d2) row(a1)? mupRup broh(c4) mow(b3) mow(b3). mow brroh(d1) row. mowmew(d2) mowmew(d2) mowruh(d3) 'aa 'aiou(a4) mRRow(b4). ma` pirp r'mow ^ra`(1).

9 PRACTICE EXERCISE

1 Here is a big mouse.
2 A mouse is nicer than a toy.
3 Is cream whiter than milk?
4 Dogs are boring (lit. 'Dogs are there').
5 You are the prettiest Cat in Christendom (careful!)
6 Don't you (C) like your food?

10 PRACTICAL EXERCISES WITH A NATIVE SPEAKER

On Sunday morning, when the Cat is in the room or on the bed with you, spread open whatever section of the Sunday paper interests you. Choose an item of reasonable but not extreme interest and read it. Read for five minutes. Has the Cat come to sit in your attention? If not, perhaps the item you are reading has excited you too much or not enough. Choose another.

When the Cat comes and sits on the paper between your eyes and the words you were reading, pause to note exactly how much and what kind of attention you were expending as you read. Trying to keep up this exact degree of attention, switch the *object* of your attention to the Cat.

If the Cat begins to purr, you have achieved a state of Positive Attention. Practise giving this kind of attention to your Cat.

At times when you want the Cat's company but the Cat is otherwise engaged, rather than subject the Cat to demanding and possibly Negative Attention, it is useful to turn the attention you have practised on to something else, such as a book or paper. You may find the Cat is not so busy after all!

Chapter Seven

The Fantasy Voice
Numbers
The subordinate connector
The universal 'it'
Impersonal Class Three verbs

MIAOWMEUH(a4)	DIALOGUE
MOW: **mow**(a1) **ma` ar miaow.** **mut.**	I am going to tell you (something). Listen carefully.
MA`: **ma`**(f 7).	I'm all ears.
MOW: **mboh mowruh**(E5) **mboh.**	A very big secret.
MA`: **ma`**(f 7)!	Yes, yes!
MOW: **mow**(a1) **ma` pra nmiaow muh**(a7) **mow broh**(a1) **arruh**(E5).	I haven't told you before that Cats see the future.
MA`: **ma` nrow**(c4) **rrow**(a3).	I beg your pardon?
MOW: (*speaks slowly*) **mow broh arruh**(E5).	Cats see the future.
MA`: (*excitedly*) **moh**(a5).	Do they really?
MOW: **moh**(E5). **mew mow ma` miaow meuh**(E4) **ruh mowrow**(c4).	Yes. I can tell you the winning lottery numbers tonight.
MA`: **mbruh mboh!**	Fantastic!
MOW: **mupRup moreh**(c4) **b'row uh b'row mRRah**(E3).	You must put a lot of money into it . . .

VOCABULARY

arruh(a5)	future, the future	**muah**(c3)	ticket
b'row uh b'row	'hairs of', i.e. lots of, many	**muh**(a7)	when, nevertheless, and, but, however, who, which, etc.; the subordinate connector
meuh(d4)	numbers		
mirr(C4)(nC)	to purchase, bring for approval, buy		
		mut(a7)	listen! pay attention!
moh(a5)	yes; indeed?		
moh(a5) **row**(a1, f 7)	to believe (be in a state of belief)	**nrow**(c4) **rrow**(b3)(nC)	'to have no whiskers', to be stupid, to beg pardon for not hearing
mowrow(c4)	winning, lucky (lit. 'Cat-having')		
mowruh(a5)	secret; Catlike	**rowb maar**(b4, d1)	to be angry, to storm, to lash one's tail
mrow(d1, b4)	to do, take, make		
mRRah(a3)	money	**urr**(b4,c4)	to choose

1 THE FANTASY VOICE

Cats have a peculiar sense of humour, and many Cats simply do not understand how difficult this sometimes makes things for humans. Throughout the eighties, for example, the present writer was given quantities of supposed data that were entirely without foundation.[1]

Fortunately, however, it is now known that Cats do not keep an entirely straight face when playing jokes. Joan Bright's discovery of the Fantasy Voice early in this decade has meant that humans can distinguish fact from fantasy once and for all, and a human with a discerning ear need never fear being made 'one of BRRow's minions', as the saying goes.

HOW IT WORKS

The Fantasy Voice is extremely simple to detect once you know what to look for. It is indiCated by a change in the Begin Note of some or all of the *nouns* in an exchange. Whatever the natural Begin Note of the word, it shifts to E. The Tonal Shape remains unchanged.

mow broh arruh(a5) – Cats can see the future

mow broh arruh(E5) – Cats can see the future
(*nudge, nudge, wink, wink!*)

FANTASY AND HUMAN ETIQUETTE

There are two ways of responding when you are in doubt as to the factual basis of what you have been told.

a. ask to have the information repeated (so that you can listen more closely)

ma` nrow rrow – I beg your pardon? (lit. I have no whiskers)[2]

b. use the 'moh' challenge

moh (a5) – really? [3]

Again, you must listen closely to the response. If the reply is **moh**[4] using

---

[1] *Cats Against the Nazis*, Bellew, 1988, has now been withdrawn from publiCation, although certain experts affect not to know this, and continue to refute arguments which have already been freely and fully withdrawn with apologies offered. (*JCAT*, Vol. 8, No. iv, p. 368, n. 3.) There is really no excuse for such behaviour. Every scholar in every discipline has made mistakes.

[2] This is a simple recognition of the fact that whiskers are a 'sense' that humans do not have, and not, as Dogfodder suggests, an impliCation that anyone without whiskers is intellectually below par. Cats often say that they are able to detect the Fantasy Voice with their whiskers.

[3] This means literally 'belief' and is short for **ma` moh row**(f 7), 'I believe it.'

[4] Short for **maaa` moh row**(f 7) – (believe it!)

the BNTP E5, you are meant to appreciate the Cat's imaginative story telling, but not to take all that she says literally.

NOTE: *High levels of excitement tend to render humans deaf to the subtle shift to Fantasy Voice. Be very very careful whenever a Cat tells you something that engages your extreme interest.*[5]

HUMAN USE OF THE FANTASY VOICE

Naturally you will be eager to use the Fantasy Voice yourself. Although grammatically it is acceptable, humans should attempt the Fantasy Voice only when they are sure a Cat is in the mood for a joke.

Do not use the Fantasy Voice to discuss a food offering that you do not actually mean to give to the Cat. This is a grammatical offence of an extremely high order (see Chapter Nine). Never, for example, say

Ø **ma` m`mow mew pirp**   –   tonight I am going to let you eat
      marr(E5)   the canary for dinner (ho ho!)

2 MEUH (NUMBERS)

Counting is based on three and nine. The basic[6] numbers one to nine are given here. For the higher numbers, the student is referred to *Cat Grammar.*

one	**me** (a2)	seven	**uhmeuh**(a2)
two	**meuh** (a2)	eight	**uhmeuh**(a2) **me**(a2)
three	**uhmeuh** (a3)	nine	**uhmeuh** (d4)
four	**uhmeuh**(a3) **me**(a2)		
five	**uhmeuh**(a3) **meuh**(a2)		
six	**uhmeuh**(a3) **uhmeuh**(a3)		

1   The numbers three and nine are considered sacred.

2   Numbers, like adjectives, may precede, follow or bracket the noun to which they refer. Nouns defined by numbers are singular.

six titbits   –   **uhmeuh**(a3) **mRRah**(a4) **uhmeuh**(a3) *or*
                   uhmeuh(a3) **uhmeuh**(a3) **mRRah**

---

[5] Hundfress's contention that, 'wenn Sie Sich an etwas sehr interessieren, kommt die Fantasiestimme nicht' (*KS*, Summer 1993, pp. 34–44) is utterly groundless. There is no example of an attested deliberate omission of the Fantasy Voice on record, in spite of numerous attempts to catch Cats out.

[6] There is another set of numbers for use among Cats, only imparted to humans as part of Tripod teachings. (See Part Four, EINSTEIN'S CAT.)

3   You may be surprised to hear a Cat singing numbers. This is connected with the sacred mystery of numbers, and cannot be further explained to humans at this time.[7] It is an offence for a non-Cat to sing numbers.

NOTE: Because the Cat sense of humour is particularly activated around numbers, it is usually best not to ask a Cat for important phone numbers, for example.

3 THE SUBORDINATE CONNECTOR

When two or more ideas are in a dependent relationship, they are joined by **muh**(f 7).

mow muh merowwap mRaow bRuh	– when a Cat is hungry, she wants food
mow ruh rowb pwah muh ma` pra bRRow(c4) **nbRRow**(a1)	– the Cat with the wet tail, whom you tricked, is not laughing
mow miaow muh marr irr row(a1)[8]	I (C) said that the canary was delicious

4 THE UNIVERSAL 'IT'

a. Passive Voice

1   The English passive voice is rendered by the use of the non-Cat form of the verb without any subject.

meuh pra urr(c4)   –   the numbers were chosen

2   Cat action is not normally rendered in the passive.

mow pra brap marr(a5)   –   the bird was eaten by the Cat (the Cat ate the bird)

3   There is one example of the Cat passive used by humans:

ma` RRow (a1)   –   I am blessed (by the Cat)

It serves as an expression of extreme gratitude, generally after an apology has been accepted. See Chapter Nine.

---

[7]   Humans have already done more than enough damage with numbers.

[8]   Note that the canary, being considered food by the time of being eaten, takes the Cat form of the verb. In a sentence such as **mow miaow muh marr 'Rowow row**(f 7), 'I said that the canary was attractive', the (nC) verb is of course used.

b. Active Voice

The universal 'it' may be used by humans as an alternate to the first person, by dropping the subject **ma`**.

> **m'mow pra mirr** (c4) **mRRah** — I bought your titbits (your titbits have been bought)

This form of all non-Cat verbs is syntactically preferable, since Cats do not distinguish human personality in quite the way we do.[9] Cats will often leave out the pronoun when speaking to you.

> **pra mirr b'row uh b'row** — did you buy lots of (lottery) tickets?
> **muah**(c3)

It is an offence, however, to leave out the pronoun 'you' when you are addressing a Cat. See Chapter Nine.

> **mow pra mRRow mew m`mew** — you were sleeping a long time

5 CLASS THREE VERBS

As in English and many other languages, there are certain impersonal verbs used to describe action not performed by anyone, e.g., 'it is raining'.

These are rendered as if they were 'Acts of Mow'. These verbs carry the BNTS D1, which indiCates neither action nor state of being, but something between the two. They are always preceded by **mow**(d4), 'the Goddess'.

> **mow**(d4) **rro**(d1) — it is raining (lit. Mow washes)
> **mow RRooww**(d1) — it is pleasant (lit. Mow purrs)
> **mow rowb maar**(d1) — it is stormy (lit. Mow is angry)

SOME UNEXPECTED CLASS THREE VERBS

Certain other verbs also take the Mow form.

> **mow**(d4) **mrow**(d1) — it has disappeared (lit. Mow has taken it.)
> **mow bRRow**(d1) — it is ridiculous (lit. Mow is laughing)
> **mow RRah**(d1) — it is offensive, or it is dangerous (lit. Mow blinks slowly)
> **mow frah**(d1) — it is dark

Many Class Three impersonal verbs also exist as Class One and Two perfect verbs; that is, there is no non-Cat form of the verb. In this book these verbs are notated (d1, a1) and (d1, b4).

---

[9] It is also admired for being self-effacing, something Cats approve of in humans.

6 COMPREHENSION EXERCISE

ma` moh row muh mow ruh rrow(b3) mowrow row? nrow rrow. marr(E5) brap 'aa m'mow Row(E4). mow(d4) rro muh mow 'aa mi'ao(a4) miaow(b4). mew pra mow frah uh rowb maar(d1).

7 TRANSLATE

1   Is that so?
2   That's unbelievable!
3   Do Cats see in the dark?
4   How ridiculous that the human believed what the Cat said about the future. The Cat was joking, but humans are stupid.
5   It is dangerous to play tricks when a Cat is engaged in the purity ritual.

8 PRACTICAL EXERCISES WITH A NATIVE SPEAKER

Playing BRRow

Hide your Cat's dinner, and tell her that she has eaten it already, plate and all. Has she recognised your use of the Fantasy Voice? If so, she will say, **bRRow**. If not, continue to play the joke. After she has protested several times, if she still does not Catch on, reveal your joke and say **bRRow(d1)**. (Do not prolong the joke beyond two or three exchanges.)

NOTE: If your Cat responds to this attempt to play BRRow with the Offended Blink, give a hasty start as if remembering that you have put it somewhere, and produce her food with no more ado. ***Do not admit having used the Fantasy Voice or apologise for playing BRRow.*** Pretend that the whole thing has been a simple mistake.

Chapter Eight

The Offended Voice
The Gentle Reproach
Early Warning
Effective responses to Early Warning

mow
uh urrt pirp maow

mow 'aa pra^ row uh urrt. mow rro rowb. mow maowrow(b4). urrt aaa`: *mow.*

mow mowruh nprih(b4). mow mra'.

urrt mow Rup(c4). urrt mow ruh ma`row truh(c4). mow broh(b4) urrt uh nbroh(b4).

urrt mow ruh prih(d2) owuh(c4). mow miaow: *maaa`.* uh(f 7) urrt 'aw. urrt ma` row. rrow nrow.

mow maow(a7) miaow: (-2) *m$\overline{aaaaa}$`.* urrt mow ruh rowb owuh.

mow m'ma` mboh maow(c7) miaow: (-4) *m$\overline{ow}$ rruh rr$\overline{ow}$b urrrt(f3) $\overline{owuh}$(c4)!*

ma` mboh rrow nrow nprih(c4).

mow truh(b4) urrt. urrt maa`row. me'a ma` mboh maow(c4). ma` aaa`: *RRow!*(c6)

mow mah(b4) m`pra^. mow mowruh mah(b4).

The Cat and the Child who Gave Offence

A Cat and a child are on the sofa. The Cat is cleaning her tail. She is singing. The child says, 'Cat.'

The Cat tolerantly does not hear. She carries on with her work.

The child touches the Cat. It ruffles the Cat's coat. The Cat blinks the Offended Blink at the child.

The child pulls the Cat's ear. The Cat says, 'Stop that.' But the child continues. It is non-Cat. It is stupid.

The Cat says irritably, 'Cut that out!' The child pulls the Cat's tail.

The Cat complains to the adult human, 'The child is pulling my tail!'

The whiskerless adult non-Cat does not hear.

The Cat scratches the child. The child sings. Now the adult human comes. 'What a pity!' it squeaks.

The Cat gets down from the sofa and majestically departs.

'aw(c4)(nC)	to continue a displeasing act
broh(b4) **uh nbroh**(b4)	to 'look and not look'; i.e. to blink at
maa`row(c4)(nC)	to sing[1]
mah(b4, c4)	to leave, depart; vaCate
maow(a7) **miaow**(b4)(C)	to speak in Second Maow
maow(c7) **miaow**(b4)(C)	to speak in Fifth Maow
maow pirp(c4)(nC)	to give offence to, insult
marr(a5)	canary; bird with strong, interesting odour
mra'(b4)(C)	to continue, carry on, carry out (usu. ritual)
owuh(c4)(nC)	to pull, squeeze, cause irritation to
praowme'a(f3)	Early Warning
prih(b4, c4)	to hear, listen
prih(d2)	ear
RRow(c6)	oversight, error; My Goodness! or What a pity!
uh(f 7)	but, although
urrt(f3)	child, offspring (nC)

I. THE OFFENDED VOICE

Everything that you have been taught so far in this book is in NMaow, the Benign or Unoffended Voice, sometimes called First Maow. You yourself will confine all communiCation to this voice. Cats, however, have access also to Maow, the Offended Voice, and it is essential that you learn to understand it.

Although grammatically there are said to be seven degrees of Maow, *practically* there are six. No one can say exactly why NMaow, the Unoffended Voice, occupies the position of first degree of offence, as Cats have so far not explained the matter.

The six levels of Maow – called by Cats **trrow**(b1) **maow** – the Ladder of Offence – all imply that something has occurred to offend the Cat. In the lower degrees, this may very often be a grammatical solecism on the

---

[1] This is the closest Cat can come to the English 'whine' or 'complain'. It is inappropriate for humans to feel or express disapproval of Cats, and Cats actually do not hear human plaint.

part of a non-native speaker.[2] Except at the extreme end – Sixth and Seventh Maow – the degrees are hard for the beginner to distinguish.[3] Learn to listen carefully.

Grammatically, each degree of Maow requires its corresponding level of apology, and to offer a lower level of apology than the Maow used is an insult (see Chapter Nine). It is best to forestall the rapid shift up the Ladder of Maow – which generally occurs when there is an inadequate response – by responding quickly with the correct level of apology.

STRUCTURE

The Offended Voice involves changes in four areas: nasality, vowel length, the **r** and **R** consonants, and Begin Note; in Sixth and Seventh Maow there are also changes in vocabulary and syntax.

a. Second Maow – The vowels are elongated and somewhat nasalised. Only practice will acclimatise your ear to these subtle variations in sound.

> **mow** (a1) **merowwap** (a1)   –   I am (still) waiting for my food

b. Third Maow – Vowels elongated and nasalised, as above. Begin Notes of entire communiCation drop one point. At this level a Cat will usually name the offence.

> (-1) **nmupRup mā` mrrew mow**   –   you (nC) must not call
>   yourself Mow

c. Fourth Maow – Glottal **R** and **RR** become palatal **r** and **rr** respectively. Increased nasalisation. Increased vowel length. Begin Note one to three points lower than Third Maow. Used in situations of physical discomfort, or where too much or not enough attention is being repeatedly offered.

> (-2) **maaa` mawrow**(b6) **bra**(c4)!   –   open this door!

d. Fifth Maow – Palatal **rr** becomes vowelised **r**,[4] loses the friCative and is elongated. Begin Note one to three points lower than Fourth Maow. Vowelisation and nasalisation as for Fourth Maow. Used in situations of grammatical, social, physical and mental irritation.

> (-4) **mow ruh rrowb urrrrt**(f3)   –   the child is pulling my tail
>   **owuh**(c4)

---

[2] Cats are, however, extremely understanding and tolerant, and will often overlook lesser grammatical solecisms on the part of a beginner because they understand how difficult the language is for the limited human apparatus.

[3] The levels have specific names in Cat, but they are difficult and not really necessary to the beginner. Those interested may consult *Cat Grammar*.

[4] Notated by **rrr+**.

e. Sixth Maow – **R** and **RR** become heavily elongated vowelised **r**. Heavy nasalisation and vowel elongation. Begin Note plummets. At this level syntax becomes distorted, and word meaning alters (often becoming intensified). Much doubling and bracketing of adjectives. Used in situations of extreme annoyance.

(-8) **'arrrra nmbrrrruh $\overline{\text{aw}}$ $\overline{\text{ma}}$`**[5]	– you are standing on my tail
nmbrrrruh $\overline{\text{awa}}$ $\overline{\text{awa}}$ m`m$\overline{\text{ow}}$	(lit. what the bleep very nasty paw
rrrr$\overline{\text{ow}}$b	non-Cat dog dog my tail?)

f. Seventh Maow – Almost incomprehensible to humans, except in intent. Begin Note, Tonal Pattern, syntax and vocabulary completely at variance with ordinary speech. Nasalisation extreme. Use of the glottal hiss. Used to express fury and threats.[6]

USE

The Offended Voice may be used only by a Cat.
As mentioned above, humans and other non-Cats are grammatically confined to the use of NMaow. You must not try to use Maow to indiCate that you are annoyed by something a Cat may or may not have done. This is a gross grammatical solecism. (See Chapter Nine, Apology.) Remember that grammar is not separable from social situations in Cat. If something is troubling you, express yourself in NMaow.

mow maor(a5) **mew**(b4)	– Cats enjoy pulling toilet paper
mbruh row uh ma`	down but sadly it makes an awful
nmbruh row	mess
mow pra brap marr(a5) **RRow**	– what a pity you mistook the
	canary for your dinner

THE DIRECT RESPONSE

At any level of Maow a Cat who has reason to believe that remonstrance is useless may abandon the Ladder of Offence and have recourse to the Direct Response, that is, biting or scratching or both.

---

[5] Note the absence of attribute marker **ruh**.
[6] It is impossible to represent Seventh Maow in the Roman alphabet. Those who are interested may see *Cat Grammar*.

2 'THE GENTLE REPROACH'

Sadly, the judging of the particular level of Maow in any instance is not quite so simple a matter as the above chart seems to indiCate. In Chapter One you have already been introduced to what Cats call the Gentle Reproach, but which humans tend to term the Offended Blink.[7] At the lower levels of Maow, this blink, roughly speaking, may be considered the equivalent of one degree of Maow. An Offended Blink on its own is usually taken to be Second Maow; an Offended Blink accompanied by a communiCation in Second Maow is obviously, therefore, not Second Maow but Third Maow; similarly a communiCation in Third Maow accompanying the Offended Blink is in effect a Fourth Maow communiCation.[8]

The offended blink

3 EARLY WARNING

Most Cats, of course, prefer not to put a human into a situation where apology and grovelling become necessary. They give what are called Early Warnings, **praowme'a**(f3), where they perceive a human about to fall into error. A careful human will not concentrate on the linguistic formulae to the exclusion of ordinary observance of Cat signals.

---

[7] A slow blink followed by turning the head away.
[8] Here the effect ceases, however. The Gentle Reproach never accompanies the higher degrees of offence. As Cats explain, it would be no favour to humans to reprimand with a milder form of reproach than the grammatical or other error deserves, for then how would we learn the right way?

a. The Tailtip Twitch – a Cat, sitting upright, her tail extended behind or wrapped around her lower limbs, twitches the tailtip slightly when she perceives a human about to commit a Maow level offence.

b. The Irritated Purr – A short burst of rough purring, possibly accompanied by pressure of the Cat's head against some part of a human's body, is a warning that the Fourth Maow offence of Too Little Attention is being offered the Cat.

c. The Extended Paw – The Cat extends the Paw of Intimacy to indiCate to the human that the offence of Failure to Make a Food Offering When Appropriate may be occurring.

4 RESPONSES TO EARLY WARNINGS

In most cases where a Cat gives Early Warning, an immediate, heartfelt communiCation in the Flattery Voice, accompanied by any small offering of food,[9] will usually put the situation to rights.

mow 'R<u>ow</u>ow r<u>ow</u>	–	how handsome you are!
mRaow	–	would you like a taste?

5 COMPREHENSION EXERCISES

urrt r'mow rrow nrow. mow uhmeuh praowme`a pra prip. mow me`a maow miaow. ma` nprih(c4). ma` prih(d2) row? moh, prih row. RRow nprih.

6 PRACTICE

1. Has the human insulted you?
2. The child has pulled her ear, her tail and her whiskers. She is extremely patient.
3. The Cat wisely did not hear the child's greeting.
4. The Cat is not speaking in Fifth Maow, though she has certainly been insulted.
5. Humans take a long time and learn nothing.
6. The child continues to greet the Cat, but the Cat continues washing her ear.

---

[9] In most instances whatever the human itself happens to be eating will be adequate.

7 EXERCISE[10]

Carefully review the story at the beginning of the chapter, **mow uh urrt pirp maow**. What Gentle Reproach was used? How many levels of the Ladder of Offence did the Cat experience and express? Did she jump any levels?

Why do you think the child ignored so many clear warnings? Notice that the adult, who clearly was within earshot, also ignored a direct complaint from the Cat. Why do you think that was?

What happened then? Was the Cat justified in its action? Is the adult or the child more at fault?

Discuss variously for a child's age of two and six years.

---

[10] No practical exercise with a native speaker is provided because of the danger inherent in deliberately causing a Cat offence. However, you are sure to do so inadvertently. Study the following chapter carefully.

Chapter Nine

Apology
Situational use of the various levels of
apology
The 'Seal of Apology'
The follow-up

ma` ruh maowpirp	To Err is Human[1]
'awarra` meuh`a mRaow(c4) **truh**(c4)	Like a mule (on a treadmill), who only moves to grind (grain)
fru(a7) **ma` ruh maowpirp meuh`a aaa`**(c4)	A human does not speak without causing distress[2]
mow mowruh(d1) **row. mow broh uh nbroh maowpirp mboh uh 'aow**	The Cat is tolerant and forgiving and takes little notice[3]
mow m`mow(a1) **maow nmiaow**(a1)	The Cat takes no personal offence no matter how grievous the error
mow mowruh(d1) **maow**(a7) **maow**(d7) **miaow**	Cats must[4] however indiCate where error has occurred
mowrrah rir rro mbo	In order to promote learning[5]
ma` ruh maowpirp nruh maow prih(d2) **pirp uh prih**(c4) **mow nmbruuh**	The worthy human gives ear and listens to Cat displeasure
fru(a7) **truh**(c4)	And mends (her grammar) accordingly

VOCABULARY

'awarra`(b1)	mule
broh prip(b4)(C)	to look for, to seek
broh pirp(c4)(nC)	to look for, to seek
fru(a7)	thus, so, behold
ma` ruh maowpirp(f1)	human, 'the non-Cat whose attribute is giving offence'
m'mow(a1) **mow**(d4) **broh pirp**[6] to apologise	

---

[1] This poem/prayer is taken from Cat teaching tales of ancient Sumer. It was taught at the third level (see Fig. 1) of learning to humans who thereafter recited it morning and evening, usually when making the Food Offering to the Mentor/s.

[2] i.e. to Cats.

[3] Lit. 'Mowlike, the Cat sees and does not see.'

[4] 'Cat nature compels' – this word may never be used by humans to indiCate a Cat duty. It is a grammatical error requiring a Level Four apology.

[5] Lit. 'the Tripod'.

[6] Lit. 'to seek the Goddess through Cat Presence'. Cats consider that a human who has erred has lost contact with Mow. Apology is not, therefore, primarily addressed to the

ma`rrah(f5)	for, in order to, for the sake of (nC)
maow(a7) **maow**(d7) **miaow**(b4)	to point out error, to speak from 2nd to 7th Maow
maow miaow(a1)(d1)	to take offence
maowpirp(f1)	error; offence-giving; sin
mowrrah(d1)	for, in order to, for the sake of (C)
mRaow(c4)(nC)	to walk, move
mrrrow(f4)	remorse
rir rro mbo	learning; arts and sciences; 'the Tripod': music, cleanliness, names[7]
rir nrow(b4, c4)	to be ashamed
rrah(b3)	purpose, intention

1 APOLOGY

In certain situations it is necessary for a human to apologise to a Cat. Students must familiarise themselves with all the levels both of the Offended Voice and of Apology. Study this chapter carefully.

RULES OF APOLOGY

1   When in doubt, apologise.

2   Follow your first apology with the Seal of Apology (see below).

3   Where there is no response from the Cat, repeat the apology, as many times as necessary, until you gain acceptance of the apology (the eating of the Seal).

4   In exceptional circumstances, a Cat may eat the Seal of Apology without actually accepting the apology.[8] This will usually be signalled by an Offended Blink after consumption of the Seal. This is called by Cats, 'Digression' or 'Digestion'.

5   *Except after a Digression,* where it should be followed by repetition of the same level of apology, if the response at any point is an Offended Blink, proceed *immediately* to a higher level of apology.

Cat. The Cat is merely a conduit for access to Mow. This is another service that Cats provide for the humans under their care.

[7]   See Part Four EINSTEIN'S CAT for a discussion of the Tripod teachings.

[8]   Usually when the Cat is particularly partial to the delicacy offered. In circumstances such as this, the gesture of eating should be seen as approving of the food *only,* i.e. the ritual of **prip pirp** (see Part Three).

6   Any repetition of an offence, whether inadvertent or deliberate, requires the apology level immediately above the one previously accepted for that offence (i.e. a *second* unbracketed mention of another Cat will require a Third Level apology).

7   You may attempt three *levels* of apology on any particular occasion.[9] If your apology is then not accepted, make no more attempt to address the Cat until the Cat speaks to you.

8   Where an apology has not immediately been accepted, the occasion of the Cat next addressing you may be taken to be an acceptance of your apology even though this is not specifically mentioned.[10]

9   Remember the Cat adage, 'True apology in a human is as rare as moderation in a flea,' and strive to be the exception.

ORDINARY OR NON-APOLOGETIC APOLOGY

NMaow (Unoffended) is the level of ordinary, everyday apology, where no offence has been given and little taken, i.e. where a Cat has not used any Gentle Reproach or Offended Voice.

ma` nruh!	–	I didn't mean it! *or*
row(f 7) **ma`**	–	I am non-Cat

are the equivalent of the English 'Sorry?' or 'Sorry!' and are used in very similar situations: i.e. where a human has not heard what a Cat has said or unwittingly touches or bumps into a Cat.

THE LEVELS OF APOLOGY

The Nine Levels of Apology may be roughly divided into three groups of three. The first three levels allow offending humans to exculpate themselves by pointing out that human genetic deficiency or experiential-based dysfunction may be the real source of the offence. Effectively they serve as gentle reminders to the Cat that a human is a human and not a Cat, and therefore, not much can be expected of you.[11] This is not unlike the general level of human to human apology.

---

[9] Do not confuse the number of *levels* with the number of *repetitions*. You may make any number of *repetitions* of a particular level of apology, until and unless the Seal is accepted or you receive an Offended Blink in response.

[10] This is a true example of Cat magnanimity and not, as Hundfress suggests, a question of absentmindedness. It should not be forgotten that in ancient India, one of the avatars of the Cat was the elephant (see Plates V and VI). This was an indiCation of the Cat's strength *and* memory.

[11] In cosmic terms, the fault is transferred to Mow.

1 **ma` ruh maowpirp row**(f 7) – I'm only human!

2 **ma` ruh maowpirp nrrow!** – It's not my fault I'm so insensitive!
   (lit. I am/humans are whiskerless)

3 **mow**(d4) **m`ma` ruh maowpirp prih 'aow prip**(d1) – It's not
   my fault I can't remember things! (lit., Mow has given me/humans
   flat ears)

The second three levels admit individual responsibility. These apologies
are based on the idea that *certain actions fall within the scope of individual
human control.* At these levels you take responsibility for your own actions.
This is a difficult concept for humans, but with time and repetition you
may become accustomed to the attitude.

4 **ma` pra urr**(c4) **nmowruh**(a3) **muh ar bRuh mowruh**(a3). –
   I chose unwisely, but I will improve.[12]

5 **mrrrow**(f4) **mboh mboh mboh muh mboh maow mboh mboh pra
   pirp m`mow. muh mow row.** – It is with enormous remorse that
   I recognise having offered great insult to you. Please forgive me.
   (lit. But you are Cat.)

6 **ma` ruh maowpirp ruh 'awaruh row**(a1) **mowruh**(a1)**rowmiow**(c4)
   uh ma`**[13] **nmeow**(c4) **muh ma` nme(a2) **m`mow**(d4). **mow**(a1) **'aa
   mow**(d4) **ma` miaow**(a1). – My error is arrogance, and I do not
   understand my relative value in the scheme of things. Please teach
   me. (lit. Cat leads non-Cat to Mow.)

The highest three levels of apology rely upon self-abasement as an
encouragement to forgiveness. Note the use of the Flattery Voice.

7 **ma` rir nrow, mrrew ruh ma` rir nrow muh m<u>ow</u>**(a1) **br<u>roh</u> ruh
   <u>mow</u>**(d4). – I am ashamed. Even my name is covered in shame.[14]
   But you are the shadow of Mow.

---

[12] Literally, 'but my intention is to desire Mowlikeness'. Cats believe that most, if not all
transgressions above a certain level betoken a failure of intent; they do not accept (or
indeed understand) the concept 'weak-willed'. If one had sincerely intended to improve,
one would have improved. Therefore the promise you make here is *to have the intention*
to improve. Again, a difficult but not impossible concept for most humans.

[13] The personal pronoun is naturally *never* omitted from an apology. There can be no
such thing as apology in the passive voice.

[14] Lit. I have no music in me. Even my name is not musical.

8 **mRRew(a3) nmah^, aw nmah^, mrrew ow nmah^ ow ow row muh mow nbroh nmah.**[15]   –   My face is dirty, my paws are dirty, my name is dirt itself. But Cat is incapable of seeing filth.[16]

9 **nb'row nmah nrrow nmrrew awarrobra(c4) ma` mboh mboh mboh 'awaruh(f3) muh m<u>ow</u>r<u>uh</u>(d1) mow(a1) m<u>ow</u>r<u>uh</u> m<u>ow</u>r<u>uh</u>.**   –   My blasphemous violation[17] is of unforgiveable magnitude and only one of your magnanimous bearing, great intelligence and goddesslike abilities could even listen to a request for absolution.

2 SITUATIONAL USE OF THE VARIOUS LEVELS OF APOLOGY

The following lists are by no means comprehensive. They are given here as guidance only, in an effort to make the student familiar with the Cat attitude to offences. There are many, many more ways of offending a Cat than could possibly be listed here. Even the assignment of levels to offences can only be offered as a general guide, since individual Cats may take a greater or lesser[18] amount of offence from any particular error, depending on what they see as the offender's state of mind in the moment the offence was committed.

The following should be studied in conjunction with the section on the Offended Voice (Chapter Eight).

1 OFFENCES REQUIRING FIRST LEVEL APOLOGY

These are normally indiCated by some form of preMaow reproach such as the Tailtip Twitch

- ❖ Minor grammatical solecisms, such as saying **ma`** too often where it may be omitted
- ❖ Relatively inconsequential errors in the Begin Note or Tonal Pattern of simple words (Note: Confusions between Cat and non-Cat BNTP are *not* considered minor, see level 5)

---

[15] This word may not take the Flattery Voice.

[16] i.e. because she is too pure.

[17] Dogfodder's alternative rendering of this term as 'naked, unclean, whiskerless, dog-licking obscenity' has some virtue as far as literalness is concerned, but is long-winded and invidious, besides imparting an air of levity to what should be treated with the utmost seriousness. Students should put this translation out of their minds when apologising at this level.

[18] Usually greater.

❖ Volunteering unwanted information about yourself (e.g. 'I'm tired today')

❖ Overuse of non-Cat adjectives and the adjectival breath

❖ Failure to respond to the Invitation to Intimacy

2 OFFENCES REQUIRING SECOND LEVEL APOLOGY

Usually signalled by an Offended Blink without any speech

❖ Mention of a Cat who is not present, without the flattery bracket

❖ Causing of mild discomfort or irritation to the Cat, such as by failing to offer a flattering description or attention where appropriate

❖ Expressing high intent where it is grammatically inappropriate (i.e. without permission)

❖ Causing a Cat to move from a comfortable position

❖ Rushing or disturbing a Cat engaged in ritual

3 OFFENCES REQUIRING THIRD LEVEL APOLOGY

Usually signalled by a communiCation in Second Maow

❖ Late or neglected mealtime

❖ Taking an unnecessary time over the preparation of the Cat's food offering *at regular mealtimes* (see below for other times)

❖ Redundancy or unnecessariness

❖ Use of Cat or perfect verbs with a non-Cat subject

❖ Failure to respond to a Cat's express desire for food, attention or any service

4 OFFENCES REQUIRING FOURTH LEVEL APOLOGY

Usually signalled by a communiCation in Second Maow accompanied by the Offended Blink

❖ Speaking to another human in Cat

❖ Too much historical enquiry into other Cats; asking a Cat (too many) questions (one may be too many)[19]

❖ Attempting to use an extended Tonal shape

❖ Making sucking or kissing noises to attract a Cat's attention instead of the grammatically appropriate approach

5 OFFENCES REQUIRING FIFTH LEVEL APOLOGY

Generally accepted as a response to Third Maow complaints

❖ Expressing or feeling disapproval of a Cat

❖ Confusion of the C and nC BNTP

❖ Using a defective verb with a Cat subject

[19] But not when the questions relate to food preferences.

❖ Mistake in the Fantasy Voice Begin Note
❖ Taking an unnecessary time to produce a promised titbit (i.e. not the regular meal)

6 OFFENCES REQUIRING SIXTH LEVEL APOLOGY

Generally accepted as a response to Fourth Maow complaints

❖ Inappropriate or too free use of the Cat's name
❖ Enquiring a Cat's Particular name
❖ Attempting to indiCate your own positive ownership of something with the word **m'ma`**
❖ Too free or inappropriate use of the word **mow**(d4)
❖ Attempting to use the imperative form of the verb to give an order to a Cat

7 OFFENCES REQUIRING SEVENTH LEVEL APOLOGY

Generally accepted as a response to Fifth Maow

❖ Addressing a Cat as 'non-Cat' (**ma`**)
❖ Using the address **mRaow** without subsequently offering food
❖ Using the true comparative or superlative to discuss the Cat
❖ Causing or allowing physical discomfort to a Cat in the first instance
❖ Persistent interference with a Cat engaged in ritual
❖ Inappropriate challenge or blatant disbelief where the Fantasy Voice may have been used by a Cat

8 OFFENCES REQUIRING EIGHTH LEVEL APOLOGY

Generally accepted as response to Sixth Maow

❖ Attempting to impose one's will on a Cat (i.e. forcing it to get off the bed or go outside)
❖ Using the Maow voice to indiCate annoyance with a Cat
❖ The use of the **'arra** form to ask a question
❖ Causing or allowing physical discomfort to a Cat after a direct complaint
❖ Use of the Fantasy Voice for humorous purposes at an inappropriate moment

9 OFFENCES REQUIRING NINTH LEVEL APOLOGY

The appropriate response for Seventh Maow communiCation

❖ Using the **'arra** form to enquire into a Cat's name
❖ Causing or allowing pain or suffering to a Cat
❖ Using the verb 'must' (**mupRup**) to a Cat
❖ Use of the Fantasy Voice to make an insincere offer of food in a misguided attempt at a joke

You will have noticed that the majority of offences entail grammatical imprecision or inaccuracy. Remember that Cats are fiercely protective of their language. This is not a question of personal arrogance,[20] but of grammatical precision,[21] which Cats see as absolutely essential.

3 THE 'SEAL OF APOLOGY'

Grammatical precision demands that all apologies be accompanied by an offering of food, preferably of a special or titbit variety.[22] Otherwise, you risk being thought insincere. Except in cases of Digression, mentioned above, the accepting of the titbit is an indiCation of forgiveness. The appropriate response to forgiveness is

ma` RRow – I am blessed

You will find that Cat forgiveness is complete. The Cat will not mention your offence again.

4 THE FOLLOW-UP

Acceptance of the apology should best be followed by a brief but intense session of Flattery Voice communiCation. The acceptance of such descriptive phrases offers the Cat further opportunity to indiCate that all is forgiven and indeed, forgotten.

fr<u>ah</u> mow(a1) **ruh ma`row** **fr<u>ah</u> uh fr<u>ah</u>**	– your fur is just as black as black![23]
mow(a1) **m<u>owruh</u>**(d1) **row**	– how magnificently Mowlike you are!

---

[20] Dogfodder, in 'The assumption of superiority as manifested in the language', *AJCS*, Vol. V, No. 3, pp. 261–90.

[21] The human explanation for the current problems of society as being caused by the breakdown of the family or of religion or by violence on television, while the matter of grammatical laxity, particularly in the English language, is entirely ignored, is laughed at by Cats. 'Grammatical laxity is the root of all ill,' is an ancient Cat proverb.

[22] And certainly not the Cat's regular meal.

[23] Note that the phrase offered here may not be used indiscriminately with any Cat. Tailor your follow-up expressions to the Cat exactly as you would any Flattery Voice comment. Be imaginative!

5 COMPREHENSION EXERCISES

'awarra` ow mew(b1) ma` ruh maowpirp. marro(a5) 'aaa muh mow
nmeow(b4). ma` ruh maowpirp 'aaa b'row uh b'row muh 'aaa: *mow
m`ma`*... mow(d4) m`mow(a1) mboh maaw(d4) mboh prip muh mow
mowruh mrow. RRow ma`! nrowb row, nrrow, prih 'aow. fru(a7) mow
mew m`mew maow pirp.

6 WRITTEN EXERCISE

1   As you (nC) speak, so shall you apologise (proverb).
2   Cat nature is forgiving (lit, Cat leads non-Cat to Mow).
3   I committed a dreadful error, but the Cat was
     magnanimous.
4   The Cat spoke in Second Maow and gave the Slow Blink.
5   The human was ashamed and apologised.

7 PRACTICAL EXERCISES WITH A NATIVE SPEAKER

Eavesdrop the next time you hear the neighbourhood Cats in debate. Can
you understand the conversation? If not, try, as best you can, to take down
what they say in writing. Ask your resident Cat to translate difficult terms.
Be sure to preface each expression you repeat with the phrase, **mow meuh`a
pra miaow** – 'then a Cat said'. Otherwise your Cat may forget that you
are quoting, and take offence if the expression is, for example, grammatically
inappropriate.

   If the Cat nevertheless responds by taking offence at any point, do not
engage in a fruitless attempt to remind her that the remarks are not your
own. Simply reply with the correct level of apology.

PART TWO

Tonality

Chapter Ten

Tonality · The Point System

INTRODUCTION TO TONALITY

Like a number of human languages, such as Chinese and Thai, Cat is a tonal language. That is, the meaning of a communiCation is indiCated not entirely by the variation of consonants and vowels that compose it, but also by the **tonal** component, or intonation pattern. This sometimes happens in English, though it may not be consciously recognised by ordinary native speakers. For example, the meaning of the speech sounds which may be indiCated by the writing signs 'Me?' and 'Me!' are really quite different. Because what we think of as the central component – the *me*-ness of the communiCation – remains the same, it is easy to overlook the fact that the first may communiCate something like 'Is it me you mean/want?' and the second 'I am the one!' English and most other so-called non-tonal languages frequently indiCate meaning through tone, so if you are a native speaker of any human language, your ear is somewhat prepared for the tonal factor which is a central meaning signifier in Cat.

Nevertheless, the extremely high degree to which tone affects meaning in Cat may make it the single most difficult feature for non-native speakers. Almost every vowel–consonant cluster in Cat has a wide range of possible meanings according to both Tonal Shape and Begin Note: some clusters have as many as four hundred different meanings. Fortunately, the use of both Tonal Shape and Begin Note is limited for ordinary conversation, and Seven Tonal Shapes and Six Begin Notes are sufficient for the beginner.

THE POINT SYSTEM

The Cat ear is a much finer instrument than its human counterpart. On the Cat scale our octave is more properly called an octogintuna,[1] signifying

---

[1] A human word that is particularly pleasing to Cats, as it carries connotations of both music and food, and suggests some of the richness of Cat, generally absent in human languages. Most words in Cat are much richer than the one-word English translation provides.

that there are eighty-one, rather than eight, notes making up the scale. These eighty-one notes are called **points** in English, to distinguish them from the tones and semi-tones of the Pythagorean scale. Each of the Pythagorean notes (do–re–mi–fa–so–la–ti–do) is a note within the octogintuna, but instead of being separated by one or two semi-tones, they are separated by up to ten points. It is difficult at first for the untrained human ear to distinguish between points, but over time and with persistence, you will find your ear acclimatising.

Chapter Eleven

The Tonal Shapes · Notation Devices

TONAL SHAPE

The intonation pattern, called the Tonal Shape, may be thought of rather as a short passage of song, where a word or syllable runs over one or more notes. Compare, for example, the intonation patterns in the English *oh, really* meaning, 'I see', with the same phrase when it means 'How dare you!' and again, when it means, 'I simply don't believe what you say.' In the last example, one syllable may move over several notes.

In inter-Cat communiCations, the number of notes per syllable is unrestricted.[1] In what may be called the 'human cluster' of Cat,[2] except for two Tonal Slides, the Tonal Shapes are restricted to no more than four notes on a syllable.[3]

In addition, in the human cluster, the tonal shape ranges generally over only two octaves. Using a Base Note[4] of Middle C, most humans will find all Tonal Shapes of the human cluster within their vocal range.

Tonal shapes are difficult at first. But take heart: you may be understood by a good-natured, well-fed Cat even if you make no distinction between points in a Tonal Shape.

NOTATION DEVICES

A **point** is signalled by the sign #, a **double-point**[5] by *. The sign + indiCates movement up the scale, the sign - signifies movement down the scale. Where there is no change from the Begin Note or the preceding note the

---

[1] The highest number so far recorded is 546 points. Many of these are so close together that they are indistinguishable to the human ear.
[2] That is, the language presented in this book.
[3] Except for Extended Tonal Shapes, but these are used only by Cats.
[4] See below.
[5] The double-point usually consists of two or three points.

mark used is the sign =. Each movement is called a **shift**. The numbers signify the number of points or double-points occurring in the shift. Thus +3# -1* -6# indiCates a Tonal Shape shifting up three points from Begin Note, down one double-point, then down another 6 points.

NOTE: Where a word has more than one syllable, a shift may sometimes, but not always, indiCate where the syllabic change occurs.

THE 7 TONAL SHAPES

Practise and memorise these patterns. If possible, ask a Cat you know well for assistance.

1. -3* -3* -3* -3* +3* +3* +3* +3*

2. == +5# +4# -2* -2# +1* -3# -3# -1* +3*

3. -4* +5* +3# +3* +2# +5# +1*

4. === -3* -3* -2*=== +2* +3* +5*==

5. ===== +4* +7* +2#

6. -1# -1# -1# -1# -1# +1# +1# +1#

7. ===============[7]

---

[7] Sometimes called the 'Bastard' Shape. Because, even in trunCation, this shape remains no more than the Begin Note repeated, it is not, properly speaking, a Tonal Shape at all. However, in action it is like a Tonal Shape and for ease is included here.

Chapter Twelve

TrunCation · Begin-and-End
Middle · Alternate

TRUNCATED TONAL SHAPE

Correct English speech, and that of many other human languages, allows for certain contractions. 'I am' may become 'I'm', 'do not' may be pronounced 'don't'. It is the same with Cat. But here we are speaking, not of a contraction in the consonant–vowel cluster, but in the musicality. That is, in the Tonal Shape.

There are three forms of Tonal Shape trunCation: Begin-and-End; Middle; and Alternate.

BEGIN-AND-END

This consists, as its name implies, of omitting the beginning and end of the Tonal Shape. Any number of notes may be omitted, *but an equal number must be dropped from the beginning and from the end.*

For example, Tonal Shape 2 in its entirety is, as we have already seen,

$$== +5\# +4\# -2^* -2\# +1^* -3\# -3\# -1^* +3^*$$

In its trunCated form, an equal number of shifts may be dropped from each end. If three are dropped, the Tonal Shape then becomes

$$+4\# -2^* -2\# +1^* -3\#.$$

If four are dropped, the shape becomes

$$-2^* -2\# +1^*,$$

and so on.

MIDDLE

As its name implies, this is the opposite of Begin-and-End trunCation. Here the notes in the middle are omitted. Again, any number may be

dropped, but they must come from the exact centre of the shape.[1]
Tonal Shape 2 might therefore become

$$== +5\# +4\# -2^* +1^* -3\# -3\# -1^* +3^*$$

or

$$== +5\# +4\# -3\# -3\# -1^* +3^*$$

or

$$== -1^* +3^*$$

but never

$$==-2^* -2\# +1^* -3\# -3\# -1^* +3^*.$$

ALTERNATE

Again the name indiCates the nature of the trunCation. Here alternate shifts are omitted from the pattern, always in a regular pattern. The count may be begun from the first shift, or the first shift may count as the first omission. Thus, every other shift being omitted from TS2 would produce the shape

$$= +5\# -2^* +1^* -3\# +3^*$$

or

$$= + 4\# -2\# -3\# -1^*,$$

depending on whether the omission begins on the first or second shift; while omitting every third would produce

$$== +4\# -2^* +1^* -3\# -1^* +3^*$$

or

$$= +5\# -2^* -2\# -3\# -3\# +3^*.$$

Any pattern of omission may be adopted, so long as it is regularly maintained. Thus a trunCation pattern of three–one would produce the shape

$$+4\# -3\#$$

or

$$=-2^* -3\#,$$

depending on where the count begins.

Non-native speakers may make use of trunCations, but beginners are advised to avoid them.

---

[1] It follows that, in an even-numbered Tonal Shape, only an even number may be omitted; in an odd-numbered, an odd number. But see Frisson, 'Allowable irregularities in truncation' [*sic*], *JCAT*, Vol. 10, No. iii, pp. 116–41.

Chapter Thirteen

Extensions
Euphony · Threnody · MagnifiCat

THE EXTENDED TONAL SHAPE

In English, in order to impress an audience with rhetoric, speakers may sometimes use larger, longer words. In particular, a speaker may call upon Latin cognates, those mellifluous, multi-syllabic words that convince the credulous that one is eduCated. Thus, if we really wanted someone to leave us alone, we would tend to use the short and succinct, 'Fuck off!' If, however, our real desire was to impress an opponent with our eloquence, we might use something closer to the schoolboy: 'Remove yourself from our distinguished presence!' Often such usage is meant to be amusing.[1]

In a similar way, Cats have access to rhetorical length, but again, the length is added to the musicality rather than the vocabulary. This usage is called the Extended Tonal Shape. Any number of tones or points may be inserted between what are called the Touchstone Notes or individual points of the Basic Tonal Shape.

Non-native speakers may not use **any** extended Tonal Shape. See Chapter 9, Apology.

EUPHONY

This is a simple extension of the Basic Pattern by repeating each note in the pattern any number of times.

Tonal Shape 3, as we have seen above, has a Basic or Touchstone pattern

$$-4^* \ +5^* \ +3\# \ +3^* \ +2\# \ +5\# \ +1^*$$

---

[1] Cats seldom use extended Tonal Shapes for purposes of amusement.

This may be extended as

$$-4^*===+5^*===+3\#===+3^*===+2\#===+5\#===+1^*===$$

It is often used in singing.

THRENODY

This is created by the insertion of any pattern of notes repeating between the notes of the Basic Tonal Shape.

Tonal Shape 1 has the Basic or Touchstone pattern

$$-{}^*3 -{}^*3 -{}^*3 -{}^*3 +{}^*3 +{}^*3 +{}^*3 +{}^*3$$

Take the three-note pattern $-{}^*8 -{}^*3 +{}^*6$,[2] and add it between each of the notes of the basic shape. Thus

$$-{}^*3 -{}^*8 -{}^*3 +{}^*6 -{}^*3 -{}^*8 -{}^*3 +{}^*6 -{}^*3 -{}^*8 -{}^*3 +{}^*6 -{}^*3 -{}^*8 -{}^*3 +{}^*6 -{}^*3 -{}^*8$$
$$-{}^*3 +{}^*6 +{}^*3 -{}^*8 -{}^*3 +{}^* +{}^*3 -{}^*8 -{}^*3 +{}^*6 +{}^*3 -{}^*8 -{}^*3 +{}^*6 +{}^*3 {}^{\,3}$$

This is sometimes used with enemies, to warn them of approaching personal disaster, or to make them aware of a hitherto unsuspected ancestry likely to have an effect on the outcome of the approaching battle. It is also used in territorial disputes.

THE MAGNIFICAT[4]

This extended shape may involve the addition of hundreds of notes to a Tonal Shape. There are many variations.[5] Generally the detail will be lost to the human ear, but the intent of the communiCation is usually self-evident. It is rare for a Cat to sing the MagnifiCat in the presence of humans.

REPEATS

Extended Tonal Shapes may be extended further through the use of compliCated repeats and slides, but this is beyond the scope of this book. Most Cats do not make use of complex extended Tonal Shapes with non-native speakers.

---

[2] This is a commonly occurring Threnody pattern, but of course any three notes may be chosen. ,

[3] The Threnody may also be added at the beginning and end of the Basic Pattern, but this form is less common.

[4] Or 'Inspired Shape'.

[5] Bright has suggested that every Cat may have an individual MagnifiCat Pattern, which constitutes the Cat 'fingerprint'. This is an extremely interesting idea, and well worth research. See 'Tonal Shape extensions as voiceprint', *JCAT*, Vol 5, No. ii, where she also suggests there may be a link between the individual MagnifiCat and the ineffable name. This seems unlikely.

Chapter Fourteen

The Begin Notes
Begin Note and Meaning

THE BEGIN NOTES

A Begin Note is just what it says: it is the musical note or tone on which
the word *begins*. Although altogether more than 46 Begin Notes exist in
Cat, as mentioned above, for purposes of conversation with humans they
may be limited to six. In addition, these range over only one octogintuna,
and are therefore accessible to all humans. In Classical Cat, they are called
the Six Begin Notes.[1] The Six Begin Notes and the language structured
around them are traditionally said to have been designed during the pre-
historic period for use with humans. Although some modern Cat theorists
now dispute this,[2] it is a compelling explanation for the curious
phenomenon of the 'cluster' pattern, whereby a large number of simplified
ideas can be expressed within the confines of those sounds capable of
being reproduced by humans. If, for example, humans were to develop a
language of communiCation between ourselves and apes, we would be
likely to choose words with many clicks and plosives, since that would
suit the vocal apparatus of the ape; and we would first develop words,
such as 'banana' and 'scratch', which expressed concepts interesting to
apes. In a similar way, Cats have limited the musicality of their language
to the human vocal apparatus.[3]

---

[1] Sometimes mistakenly called 'The Vulgar Begin Notes'. This idea has arisen through a
misreading. The word is **meuh** (a3) (six), not **ma`uh** (f 7) (corrupt, vulgar, human).

[2] For example Dogfodder, 'The vulgar notes – use or abuse?' *KS*, Winter 1996, in which
the author suggests that far from being designed for comprehension by humans, the
Six are simply what Cats consider 'a crude area of sound'. According to this theory, the
fact that they are also the normal range for human voices is at best, coincidental, and at
worst, a commentary on Cats' attitudes to human beings.

[3] The conceptual base of the language has been designed around our intellectual
limitations.

THE SIX BEGIN NOTES

The Begin Notes given here are for human use; in Cat use they may vary. The Base or Central Note is Middle C. Remember that the use of the first six letters of the alphabet is for convenience only. These letters do not represent the musical notes.

a – Middle C or Base Note	**d** – 9 points above a
b – 3 double-points above a	**e** – 4 points above a
c – 3 double-points below a	**f** – 13 points below a

BEGIN NOTE AND MEANING[4]

Although much more research is needed on the subject than what has so far been undertaken, it seems worthwhile to mention here that, as far as can be seen, each of the six (and perhaps each of the 46) Begin Notes carries a general cluster of meaning. Until more is discovered of the Cat worldview, some linkages will remain mysterious. But the following may be of some assistance to the self-taught.

a – words which begin with Begin Note A seem to carry ideas of diversity and richness; birth, fertility; beauty and pleasure; age, wisdom, and death. Grammatically Begin Note A is mostly reserved for speech relating to Cats and food.

b – words denoting (Cat) action, including many verbs; concepts of vigour, positive attributes

c – words with a negative or neutral meaning, words denoting certain non-Cat action

d – carries overtones of oneness, indivisibility; divinity; particular, as opposed to general femaleness; cleanliness. The vibration of the D-note as a sound is said to include the vibration and thus the concepts of all the other notes except F. Thus the unity of D includes the diversity of A, and not vice versa. More research into the Cat worldview will undoubtedly makes such ideas clearer.

e – used in the Fantasy Voice

f – includes ideas of chaos and disruption; limitation; grammatically it is used in non-Cat verbs, nouns and pronouns, and may be considered the 'opposite' or 'completion' of Begin Note A[5]

---

[4] This is a brief survey only. For a fuller discussion of these see my *The Begin Note's Role in Meaning*, Bellew, 1988.

[5] This is, however, not, as Dogfodder would have it, the 'Negative Note'. Anyone who imagines Cats consider chaos a negative, for example, has only to examine a bathroom after a Cat has been rearranging it.

Chapter Fifteen

The Base Note
Establishing the Base Note
Purr Note and Base Note

THE BASE NOTE

Except for those speakers who have particularly deep or high voices, human students of the language should always use a Base Note of Middle C. However, Cats have widely different vocal ranges. Siamese, for example, tend to have rather deeper voices than Persians. The *interval* between the Begin Notes will always be consistent, but the Base Note itself may vary from Cat to Cat. The Cat's Base Note will then take the place of Middle C in the chart on page 106 above, and all the other Begin Notes must be taken *in relation to the Base Note.*

ESTABLISHING THE BASE NOTE

The Mow Method   It is necessary to establish the Base Note of any individual Cat before communiCation can take place. This may usually be achieved by listening attentively when the Cat greeting **mow**(a1) is pronounced, since, because of its context, this greeting can never be confused with any other word. *The Begin Note of mow*(a1) *is the Cat's Base Note.* By referring to the chart, the student will be able to place the other Begin Notes in the speech of that particular Cat.[1]

PURR NOTE AND BASE NOTE

An alternative method of establishing a Cat's Base Note has recently been

[1]   Self-taught students are advised to converse with one Cat only for the first few months of their studies. This refines the ear, and establishes an appreciation of the intervals between the Begin Notes. Students who speak to Cats with differing vocal ranges too early in their studies may find that their ear gets confused. Classroom teachers are advised not to bring more than one visiting Cat lecturer to the classroom during the first two terms of study.

suggested, which may be useful for some students. It is not effective with all Cats, and the student is advised to be cautious in applying this method.

First, find the Purr Note.[2] This note, like the Base Note, varies from Cat to Cat. Since a purr is usually a blend of eleven notes ranging over one tone, care must be taken to establish the *lowest* note of the purr. Count fifteen double-points up from the Purr Note, then one point down. This method is successful with highly contented, unassuming Cats. It may not be used with most Siamese, whose voices, as mentioned above, tend to be deeper in relation to the Purr Note, and who anyway are rarely contented or unassuming. Use the Mow Method for establishing the Base Note of any Cat with a deep speaking voice.

---

[2] This method is not recommended for use with Cats who have a very breathy or asthmatic purr, as the Purr Note may be difficult to establish.

PART THREE

Music, Myth and Legend

Music

Cats brought the concept of music to humankind. In Cat myth music is said to be a manifestation of the Goddess **Mow**, and Cats, unlike humanity, have always had music. Cat legend records the giving of the gift to humanity. That Cats are justified in their assessment that this gift predated that of fire is given substance by the remarkable fact that no legend of any kind records the gift of music in human history, while the gift of fire is still remembered in the Greek legend of Prometheus. It is well known that the Greek legends were originally sung.[1] Thus, the legend of the bringing of fire must have been recorded *after* humankind was given music. The gift of music may have predated that of fire by many millennia.

All musical notes exist in the Cat scale. As the teaching of music continued through the generations, and especially post-Cataclysmically,[2] it was observed that humans were ill-equipped to understand the full musical scale, and adjustments had to be made.

In various parts of the world, Cat Teachers 'toned down' the musical scale for human consumption, according to the state of the particular group of humans any individual Cat was working with.

Pythagoras

That Pythagoras had a Cat mentor is considered by Cats to be certain. Her name was Hermestris Magistra,[3] and her task was to introduce a new, abbreviated musical scale to humans in the aftermath of the Cataclysm. The Pythagorean scale is that scale, and it is that which is used as the basis for this book, since it is assumed that most readers will be familiar with it. However, it should be noted that the Pythagorean scale, like all other scales, is only what Cats call a 'rough approximation' of the Cat scale, and indeed, is often considered to be almost too degraded to be of use. Certain limited ideas can be expressed through this scale to aid in the advancement

---

[1] W. B. Stanford, *The Sound of Greek*, Berkeley, University of California Press, 1967.
[2] See Einstein's Cat.
[3] 'Teacher of the Three Secrets'.

111

of humanity in the West, but this would be insufficient on its own. Without the additional expression of Eastern scales, the environment necessary to the development of humanity could not occur.

The Cat Scale

It has been mentioned elsewhere in this book that violinists will find the study of Cat less difficult than many humans. Violins are capable of playing more of the notes in the True or Cat Scale than most instruments, and for this reason Cats love to hear the violin. If you are a violinist you may find that your resident Cat encourages you to play for her.

It will be obvious to most readers by this time that a violin is capable of actual Cat speech.[4] In particular, it has been suggested that a violin is capable of playing a Cat's 'deep and inscrutable, singular name'.[5] It may be the case that when a Cat sings along with a violin, it is because this name is unconsciously being played by the violinist. However, no Cat has yet been induced to comment on this theory.

The black notes on the piano are also particularly pleasing to Cat ears. These notes are less abased than the white notes, and are coloured black because they are closer to sacred than other notes. This is thought to be a reflection of the colour of the Mow's fur.[6] Black notes on the piano will also sometimes play meaning, generally something ludicrous. That is why the black notes are said to make a Cat laugh.

---

[4] Though not, of course, in the 'human cluster'.
[5] By Bleat. See the section on names in Chapter Five. Because of the high degree of secrecy still surrounding names, this thesis is likely to remain without proof for some time.
[6] See Chapter Three.

The Legend of Canopus

The Coming

According to the oldest Cat legends, Cats arrived on earth many thousands of years ago from the star Canopus. Cats had the task of overseeing evolution on the planet. Their mission was to seek out any species capable of progress and establish communiCation and, ultimately, teaching academies.

Since music has an important civilising influence on the brain of most species as well as being essential for understanding Cat, introducing the concept of music was the first task Cats set themselves. At first the focus was on birds as being the most susceptible to this influence. Birds were scientifically dissected and their advanced vocal chords noted;[1] furthermore, they were quick to understand the principle of bathing.

But in spite of these great advantages, birds would not accept the most significant of the Laws of Cleanliness: the Law of Burial of Waste. Even worse, water birds actually disposed of their waste in water[2] – which had been designated their Substitute Cleansing Substance when the inadequacies of their salivary systems was discovered. This so horrified Cats that birds were subsequently classified as a food species.

The Gift

'**Arramowarra**, 'The Cat Whose Name is Unknown', was a ginger-coloured female Cat. She took an interest in a group of humans who had invaded her hunting area, observing them more and more closely, although proximity to humans was at that time considered pollution. One day 'Arramowarra suggested to her group that the humans were worthy of

---

[1] Some say that birds' abilities were discovered accidentally, over dinner; but this is mere vilifiCation.

[2] It was only later that humans began to do the same thing, and it was realised that this was a perversity peculiar to the planet. But it was by then too late to begin over with birds. In any case, Cats were reluctant to do so because birds are very tasty.

assistance. There is no modern parallel that can be drawn to suggest the enormity of this proposition. Humans, with their grotesque vocal sounds and their bodily filth, were considered almost beyond redemption. It was assumed by many Cats that humans were inadequate and would die out.

From her observations, however, 'Arramowarra came to believe that humans might be trainable. No record exists of exactly what she based this opinion on, but her group regarded the idea with horror. When it was discovered that 'Arramowarra was pregnant, it was feared that she would raise her kittens in her own beliefs and thus create a faction within the community.

'Arramowarra was expelled from the group. She went out into the wilderness, nested, and prepared to give birth. 'Arramowarra was experienced at birthing, having produced many fine litters; but, perhaps because of the terrible stress that accompanied it, this birthing became compliCated. 'Arramowarra nearly died.

As she lay suffering, a human female heard her cries and discovered her nest. 'Arramowarra asked for food and water, and although it is unlikely that the human female actually understood language at that point, she none the less brought 'Arramowarra water and a meal of uncooked animal flesh.[3] She nursed 'Arramowarra through the birth, and eight of 'Arramowarra's ten kittens were saved.

'Arramowarra stayed with the human female and began to teach her music. Through this woman, called in legend Ma`RRuh^(f5), 'Virtuous Human', music was passed to humanity.

'Arramowarra's eight kittens grew up among the humans, and were worshipped by them as gods. Daily the humans commemorated their first meetings with Cat Presence by ritual offerings of water, milk and meat – a ritual not abandoned by humans even today.

After her death, her eight daughters carried on the work of teaching music, cleanliness and other basics to humans as a first step to other teachings, and the number seven came to be sacred to humans.[4]

---

[3] That there is no mention here of the ritual of the Offering of Warmth, or of *cooked* flesh, is evidence that the gift of music predated that of fire. See EINSTEIN'S CAT.

[4] That is, subtracting one ('Arramowarra) from eight, rather than adding. To Cats it is the number Nine that is sacred. It is possible that the number of daughters is metaphorical. Dogfodder suggests no more than five, but there is no particular evidence for this.

The Nine Blessings

Cats are often misunderstood by humans, but nowhere more consistently or more unproductively than in the area of the Nine Blessings.

By tradition, each of the Nine Blessings was a gift from one of 'Arramowarra's kittens,[5] each of whom gives her name to the blessing; the last is attributed to 'Arramowarra herself.

1. The Blessing of Aw Mawrow

Known as 'The Paw at the Threshold', this is a much misunderstood household blessing ritual which entails hovering at an open door and crossing back and forth over the threshold one or several times. This brings good luck on a household by 'opening the door' or 'cleansing the path', and should ideally be performed once every twenty-four hours, more often as needed. Humans do themselves no favours by inhibiting Cats in the performance of the ritual.

2. The Blessing of Rowbrro

'Purifying the Tail'.[6] While seated, the right or left hind leg is lifted at an angle of between 45 and 90 degrees to the ground, and the area under the tail ritually washed. Humans who find this particular ritual an annoyance are a great trial, as this is every Cat's ritual observance to Mow. A resident Cat who was not herself 'in good odour' with Mow would bring scant blessings on any household she visited. Humans should not interfere with a Cat performing this ritual, by, for example, demanding that a Cat get down from the bed to do it. Cats must choose specific times and places for such rituals, and human preferences in the matter can generally only be ignored.

---

[5] They more likely derive from the daughters of the Goddess Mow, who also are said to number eight. The confusion goes back to earliest times.

[6] **rowb**(b6) refers to the tail, its fur, and adjacent working parts.

3. The Blessing of Pra^ Truh

Literally, 'Kneading the Sofa'. This was originally done on the straw, canvas or wooden walls or doors of the human abode, and performed a similar function to 'The Paw at the Threshold', i.e. encouraging 'Cat winds' to blow luck into the house. Nowadays necessity[7] dictates that it be performed indoors, where it is often less effective, for obvious reasons. Nevertheless, Cats carry out the ritual for whatever benefits may still accrue to humans.[8]

4. The Blessing of MRRow

Or 'Communing with Mow'. This is the Sleep Ritual, and is among the most sacred Cat observances. There is no explanation yet of the phenomenon many people have noticed, whereby some Cats regularly choose the same geographical loCation for the performance of this ritual and others will fall into it at various loCations all over the house. At this time Cats can only say that it has to do with the specific properties of a given house.[9]

---

[7] Because of the nature of most modern doorposts.

[8] Some Cats consider the action more effective when a carpet near an external doorway is kneaded; most, however, agree that the ritual must be performed with the Cat in an upright, two-legged posture.

[9] Chang is engaged on a comparative study of MRRow postures and Feng Shui. The results were sadly not available at the time of going to press.

5. The Blessing of Prip Rowb

'Presenting the Tail'.[10] Cats expose the area directly under the tail to each other as an important expression of shared Mowness. At this time an attempt is being made worldwide to encourage human engagement in this important ritual. Humans who resent Cats' presenting of their anus for the ritual greeting[11] merely expose their own lack of evolutionary potential. The proper, evolved response is, of course, to place the nose to the anus and sniff, though many Cats despair of humans ever learning it.[12]

6. The Blessing of Frow

'Frow' is a term used to describe sacred burial of food originally offered to Mow which has passed through the Cat digestive system. It carries special resonance when carried out in a garden that borders on the garden in which the Cat is principally resident.

7. The Blessing of Pew

Or 'Rain'. This ritual, which has been adduced by some scholars as evidence that one at least of 'Arramowarra's offspring was male,[13] involves extruding sacred Cat substance onto plants and inanimate objects. Mistakenly considered by many humans to be a form of territorial marking, the blessing of rain, on the contrary, marks out holy ground – sacred enclosures within which Cats may perform other necessary rituals.[14]

8. The Blessing of Maow Praow

Maow Praow developed this ritual through close understanding of the story of BRRow and the Parrot (see below). Called the 'Pursuit of the Apparently Inanimate', such rituals as chasing bits of string and crumpled

---

[10] See note 6.
[11] For example, Guthound. See 'The nine indignities', *CK*, 8, No. ii, pp. 77–90.
[12] 'Even *dogs* have got that far,' as one source expressed it.
[13] Toadie, 'Subtext in the nine blessings', *JCAT*, Vol. 7, No. iv, pp. 11,634–715.
[14] cf. the concept of *eruv*.

paper are actually necessary to destroy hostile entities which would otherwise threaten the human environment.

9. The Blessing of 'Arramowarra or Prip Pirp [15]

Literally 'Granting the Offering', it actually signifies the acceptance of an offering. It is a ritual imposed on all Cats who interface with humans. They are required to assess all human offerings of food to the Goddess Mow for purity of content *and intention*. Only wholesome offerings which are deemed by the Cat to be made from a pure heart may be accepted. An accepted offering confers a blessing on the human who has made it, but humans who resent a Cat's rejection of their offering would be better engaged in focusing on their own shortcomings.[16] To have an impure offering accepted would offend Mow and risk bringing her rage down upon the human donor.

---

[15] Toadie suggests that this may be 'Arramowarra's true Particular name, because it so neatly follows the pattern of the particular names of her daughters being devolved upon the blessing each bestowed (Toadie, *JCAT*, op. cit., pp. 6–8). This is an engaging hypothesis, but without sufficient foundation. 'Arramowarra must have had a name *prior* to her acceptance of the human female's offering, and that is her true name. Even if she did take the name Prip Pirp to commemorate making contact with a viable human, it would give no clue. The mystery of just who 'Arramowarra was, is, sadly, not so easily solved as this.

[16] Here again, the degree of human misunderstanding of the ritual is very high. Ignorant and unfounded comments such as that by Guthound: 'Quelles que soient les origines de ce rite, pour la plupart des chats modernes il ne représente qu'un simple prétexte à la gourmandise,' only exacerbate the situation. 'Violation des principes sacrés: signe de décheance morale chez les chats domestiques', *CH*, 1995, p. 568.

*Posthumous portrait of the author's Cat tutor, Johnny, engaged in the ritual
of Aw Mawrow. (Drawn by Philip Snow)*

Other Legends

The Trickster

When humans say something would make a Cat laugh, we are referring, though most of us don't know it, to BRRow, the Trickster.

BRRow is Mow's son, the only male demi-god in the pantheon. However, he is not a tom; he is unable to sire. There is some evidence to show that maleness is incompatible with divinity among Cats, and it may be that BRRow has only managed to be admitted to demi-divinity by the sacrifice of his sexual (but not his psychological) masculinity.

There are numerous stories about the tricks BRRow has played.

The Story of BRRow and 'Aa[1]

BRRow liked to play tricks from an early age. He had eight[2] sisters and was always playing tricks on them and his mother. One night when BRRow was sleeping after a day of tricks, 'Aa, his sister, took his testicles from him. She placed them on her own eating dish. In the morning, she said to BRRow, 'I have hunted and found some very tasty delicacies. Do not eat them, for they are only for me.'

BRRow went to 'Aa's eating dish and ate up what he found there. 'Aa saw that the dish was empty. She laughed. 'You think you have tricked me,' she said.

---

[1] To read a version of this story in Cat, see Chapter Three.
[2] Note that the combined total of Mow and her daughters is thus nine. BRRow can therefore not truly be considered part of the Godhead, as his presence would bring the number up to ten.

BRRow cleaned his sexual parts[3] in satisfaction after his meal. When he discovered that he had no testicles, he understood how 'Aa had tricked him. He laughed. He said, 'That is an excellent trick. Now I will trick others until I have played a trick as good as the one 'Aa has played on me.'

Every kitten born has one hair from BRRow's pelt somewhere on her body.[4] In this way BRRow is still playing tricks, and he will do so until he has invented a better trick than the one 'Aa played on him.

That is why, when a Cat has played a trick, she says, BRRow.[5]

[3] The fact that it is BRRow and not one of his sisters who is shown in the act later given to humanity as the Blessing of Rowbrro is insufficient grounds for suggesting, as Dogfodder has, that it is not a ritual but only a joke played on credulous humanity. If he cannot do better than this in his obsessive attempts to degrade what he cannot understand, perhaps he should move to an area of study that is within his intellectual and moral grasp, if one can be found.

[4] Often on the forehead or around the ears. The loCation of this BRRow hair may sometimes be established through the fact that, as might be expected, it is a spot that needs frequent gentle scratching. Some Cats say that when humans are stroking or scratching a Cat, they are 'hunting the BRRow spot'. Although not one of the Nine Blessings, (which can only be performed by Cats), this is considered by Cats to be a human activity (like the food offering) which confers a blessing on the human who performs it.

[5] This sound is the equivalent of the English 'Ha ha'. Some say that whenever a Cat laughs, it is because any joke reminds her of the 'First Joke': the trick 'Aa played on BRRow. Cats sometimes laugh when a human scratches their BRRow hair.

BRRow and the Parrot

A parrot was sitting in a tree, cracking nuts. The shells of the nuts fell on the ground beneath the tree. BRRow came along. When he approached the shells they leapt away from him. BRRow attacked and killed some of them.[6] He was very fierce; the parrot grew frightened.

'Why are you killing the shells?' the parrot asked BRRow.

BRRow did not wish to tell the parrot that it was merely for sport. 'I overheard them talking about you, my friend,' he said. 'What they said disturbed me so much that I could not restrain myself.'

The parrot got excited and flew to the ground. 'What were they saying about me?'

'They said,' said BRRow, leaping upon the parrot and sinking his teeth into its back, "a parrot is as delicious to a Cat as a nut is to a parrot".'

[6]   cf. The Blessing of Maow Praow, above.

PART FOUR

Einstein's Cat

A Brief Overview of the
Evidence for the Influence of
Cats on Human Social,
Intellectual and Evolutionary
Development from Earliest
Historical Times to the Present

NOTE

The original research published here was conducted between August 1965 and June 1996 in various private residences and alleyways in Toronto, London, Fethiye, Jerusalem, New York and Aberystwyth.

LIST OF INFORMANTS

Toronto

Johnny, a white neutered male with a smudge of black on the back of his head, of Siamese build. A generalist, as well as oral historian of the Cataclysm and Post-Cataclysmic period.

Medico, a seal-point Siamese, with a crook in his tail and cross-eyed, whose area is Names. He was also enormously patient in elucidating the Nine Blessings.

Rufus, a black long-hair neutered male. An extremely long-winded oral historian of Pre-Cataclysmic period.

Fluffy, black, fluffy, mother of Rufus. An authority on human historical figures and their Cat mentors.

London

Pussum, a grey and black tabby, partial to milk and lightly boiled salmon. An expert on all forms of greeting.

Puffin, black female with white forepaws and nose.

Floyd 'Fancyman', all grey, very affectionate, initiated me into the mysteries of Intimacy.

Fethiye

Kara, all white, uncertain age, 'feral'. Mostly a source of curses and abusive terms.

Cal, black and white. Oral historian of legends and myths.

Jerusalem

Bathavah, grey (or perhaps white), advised on numbers and other esoteric wisdom, as well as the protocol of food offerings.

New York

Beetle, all black, once 'feral', who returned to human mentoring after experiencing a call when he was offered food by a human.

Aberystwyth

Margaret, orange and white, historian of the conCatenation.

Sophy, pure white. Direct descendant of Timaeus.

Einstein's Cat

(The following is the text of a paper delivered at the Annual Congress of Cat Studies at Bachgarten Fintz during the full moon of August 1996. Those whose only interest is the practical speaking of Cat may omit this section with a clear conscience.)

Foreword

Cats say that 'history makes Cats laugh'.[1] That is because humanity's determined rooting through the past is seen as misguided and a waste of effort. Humans would do better to live in the moment, as Cats do. It is precisely to discourage this kind of trawl through the past that Cats have been careful through the ages to leave little concrete trace of their interaction with humankind. For most of human history, for example, with few exceptions, humans have been forbidden to represent their Cat mentors in art. This makes the historian's job difficult, of course, but so much prolonged influence over such a span could hardly remain invisible, and for those who know what they are looking for, the evidence is unmistakable.[2]

The First Cat-Human Contact

Cat remains have been found in human settlements all over the world since the end of the last Ice Age. Since it is impossible to tell whether these remains were of 'wild' or 'tamed' Cats, mammal life experts are uncertain as to whether they are evidence of the so-called 'domestiCation of the Cat' or of the fact that Cats were 'valued for their pelts'.[3]

Cat oral historians, on the other hand, are unanimous in declaring this period 'The Undertaking of the Task', when Cats first began to interact with humans for the purpose of guiding their evolution.

The fossil record supports this view. It indiCates that, according to

---

[1] **mow**(a1) **maowr**(a5) **brah**(f 7) **bRRow**(a1). Johnny, 2.9.95; 11:15.
[2] All known Cat records of Cat interaction with humans are oral.
[3] J. Clutton-Brock, *Domesticated Animals*, p. 111. The latter hypothesis is, of course, ridiculous.

current palaeontological dating,[4] Cats evolved into their present form many millions of years ago, and long before humans arrived at their own present form. Furthermore, *no significant change occurred in Cats as they began associating with humans.*

Genus *homo*, on the other hand, has experienced profound evolutionary changes since the first contact between human and Cat. This significant fact has been entirely overlooked by most human experts.

Cats, in fact, first made contact with humans between 10 and 15,000 years ago, approximately simultaneously with the appearance of what humans call *homo sapiens*.[5] Cats refer to this stage of development in humans as *femina linguam Cata loquens*. According to Cats, we have not yet reached the stage of *homo sapiens*.

Since that time, with a few tragic lacunae, Cats have been attempting, with greater or lesser success, to guide and assist human evolution on earth.

The Tripod

Cat teachings from earliest times have been based on what Cats, and many ancient human communities, have termed the 'Tripod'.[6] This Tripod consists, as the name suggests, of three laws, or arts:[7] the Law of Music,[8] the Law of Cleanliness[9] and the Law of Names.[10,11]

These form the basis, but they by no means preclude the possibility of other, simultaneous development. On the contrary, many of humanity's great advances were by-products of the teaching of the Tripod Arts.

An example is fire. The gift of fire was given to humanity[12] because

---

[4] Which is wildly wrong. Current theories on the span of life on earth overestimate by a factor of at least ten, and probably one hundred.

[5] Johnny, op. cit. 14:07.

[6] This section is a composite of information gained in several interviews, held separately, with Johnny, 3.9.95 and 6.9.95, and with Rufus, 11.9.95 and 12.9.95 (an overnight interview) and 23.9.95.

[7] The word **mih**(d4) has no direct translation in English. Its meaning would be partially conveyed by the phrase art-science-learning-sacred.

[8] **rir**(d4).

[9] **rro**(d5).

[10] **mbo**(d2).

[11] 'The fourth leg is numbers.' Since a tripod by definition cannot have four legs, the 'fourth leg' can only be that of the one who, having gained understanding of the Tripod, is now 'standing' upon it, ready for advanced teaching.

[12] Through drawing the attention of humans to the sparks that occur when a Cat is vigorously caressed. Humans were encouraged to see the connection between such sparks as these – associated with the warmth of the Cat's body – and the sparks created when flints were struck against each other during the manufacture of tools.

humans who are cold have a short attention span.[13] In a similar vein, little could be taught to humanity without the use of language.

The three Tripod Laws are intimately interconnected, but human societies are not always susceptible equally to all of them.[14] As a general rule, where any one of the three Tripod Sciences pertains in a given culture, we may suspect Cat involvement at that point. Where two or more Tripod Arts obtain simultaneously or in neighbouring cultures, we can be sure that an assumption of Cat influence will not be wrong, and other developments in the culture at that period may be attributed to the by-product effect. When all three appear,[15] Cat involvement is certain.

The PreHistoric World[16]

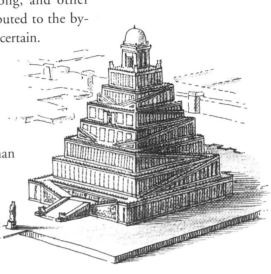

In earliest times, Cat influence pervaded entire cultures. Almost all women, and many men, could understand ordinary Cat speech, and Cats were revered as teachers. During this Golden Age, numerous advances in the human community resulted from Tripod teachings.

What humans call 'The Birth of Agriculture', for example, arose because of Cats' well-known attachment to place. A Cat attached to a particular

1 Ziggurat school showing the seven levels of classroom, the domed eighth level being the residence of the Cat teacher. The ninth level is ineffable. After Chipiez.

[13] In his seminal essay, 'On the Relations between Pasht, the Moon, and the Cat, in Egypt' (in *Transactions of the Society of Biblical Archaeology*, Vol. VI, London, 1878), Hyde Clarke has most significantly shown that 'the cat must have been known to man and have been named at least as early as the origin of language'. It will be noted that the structure of Cat is Indo-European (that is, the language as presented in this text. As mentioned elsewhere in this book, this 'non-Cat interactive speech' has been developed primarily for use with humans. High Cat, the broader language base from which the language we call Cat has been drawn, is *not* Indo-European. As far as can be ascertained at the moment, High Cat contains elements of many, if not all, human language types. There is some reason to believe that in earliest times, several varieties of Cat were developed for use with different groups of humans around the world. To date, however, only the one presented here has been revived. We await with interest the results of the work of D. Chang, a Chinese linguist, who is attempting to uncover evidence for an ancient 'Chinese' Cat).

Whether Cats adapted the shape of Cat to a language which our Indo-European forebears were already speaking in order to communiCate with them, or whether the Indo-European language can itself be traced back to Cat origins, is still a subject of debate. But it may well be, as Hyde Clarke seems to suggest, that language itself is a gift from Cats to humanity.

[14] At the moment modern, and particularly Western, 'civilisation' is incapable of understanding Names.

[15] It is unfortunately very difficult for modern human researchers to see where the Law of Names has been employed in a culture (see note 14).

[16] This section is a brief abstract of remarks made to the author by Rufus on 12.10.95; 11:08–22:17.

tribe of hunter-gatherers would remain, say, at the tribe's summer habitat year-round, so that at first Cat instruction was seasonal. A desire on the part of the tribal members to stay in the same locality permanently for the sake of being close to the Tribal Tutor naturally encouraged the development of agriculture.[17]

Urbanisation, seen by most anthropologists as a mysterious phenomenon requiring elaborate explanations such as population growth, etc., was the direct result of fluctuations in the number of Cat mentors available in various areas at different times.[18] In order to maintain continuity of the teaching at such times, it was necessary to establish formal schools, where each Cat mentor could serve a much larger group than had previously been necessary. As more groups lost their mentors and came to settle in the vicinity of a school, urbanisation occurred. Once the fourth leg, Numbers, had been introduced into a society,[19] it was possible to build a physical structure to contain such schools,[20] and so institutional architecture was born.

Pottery and metal-working arose through the natural human desire to present their offerings to Mow in bowls and cups (Fig. 2). And so forth.

2 Pottery bowl from Harappa. The development of pottery arose out of human worship of Mow. The fish design indiCates that the bowl was for offerings to Mow (i.e. giving food to a Cat). After Gordon.

---

[17] It is suggested by Cats that planting seeds may have been due to a human misunderstanding of Cat teachings on cleanliness. According to this theory either Cats, attempting to teach humans to dispose of their excrement, inadvertently included a seed in the burial, or undigested seeds in buried human excrement germinated. To Cats, this is humorous if exasperating evidence of the perversity of the human mental system – that we entirely lost sight of the *actual* lesson, and pounced upon an entirely incidental side-effect. Cat teachings tend to have such beneficial side effects, but Cats would prefer it if humans grasped the central lesson first. Cats call this kind of thing, 'sniffing the nose before the tail'.

'Only humans would dispose of their waste in their own cleansing and drinking fluid [water] and then manufacture artificial waste to bury with their seeds.' Johnny.

[18] The reasons for which are beyond the scope of this essay.

[19] A tragic error, as it later proved, and one which Cats deeply regret. See below.

[20] In the shape of a ziggurat (Fig. 1). This structure, about which so much has been written and surmised, was simply a formal Tripod School (built on a square because of the introduction of the 'fourth leg'). The various levels of the structure contained classrooms (so-called 'shrines') which were devoted to various levels of the teaching. The reason for the diminishing size of the levels is simply that fewer and fewer people were capable of progressing through the levels. This is the origin of the term 'higher learning'. There were eight physical levels; the ninth level was ineffable. Cats undoubtedly had their living quarters in the 'temple' at the eighth level, indiCating their ability to commune with the ninth level. It has been suggested by Nathan ('Khataltoulot ha 'Arramowarra wa Erech ha Beit Sefer ha Khatzouveh beh Sumer' *CK*, Vol. II, No. 3), that the eight levels are a reference to the eight kittens of 'Arramowarra (see Part Three), which is a charming, if not adequately defended, idea.

The Early Historical Civilisations

Sumer   Evidence that inhabitants of early Sumer held Cats in the highest esteem is found in a statue from the Ubaid period (4th millennium BCE) of a Cat-headed female holding a kitten in her arms (Frontispiece). This figure is probably a votive statue of Mow, the Cat goddess.[21] Oiseau has pointed out the significance of the hat hiding the ears: '*Bien que les oreilles de la déesse soient, d'un point de vue mystique, différentes des oreilles des chattes, elles sont cachées de vue. Celles qui comprennent n'ont pas besoin d'une image; ceux qui ne comprennent pas n'en ont pas le droit.*'[22]

Those who suggest that the statue is a 'Cat-headed woman', i.e. a human versed in Cat teachings to the extent of being mentally evolved into a Cat, have never substantiated their case.[23] It is abundantly clear from evidence elsewhere that the 'Cat-headed' were never considered to have acquired the divine ears, and there would therefore be no need for the disguising hat.

Impressive linguistic evidence that the foundations of early dynastic Sumer rested firmly on Cat teachings is found in the cuneiform symbol for the Sumerian *sa'a*, Cat. This is a complex of two word signs, *sa*, 'string', and *a*, 'water'[24] (Fig. 3). Since the word 'string' is the same word as that used to denote the strings of a lyre, *music* and *cleanliness* are actually incorporated in the *name* for Cat[25] – a remarkably neat way of indiCating that all three concepts were being taught in this culture.

A flat, roughly equilateral triangular stone about a foot long on each side,[26] probably also fourth millennium, has been found near the library of Sumer. On the reverse, at each apex, a small round hole indiCates that the stone must once have formed the top of a tripod. On the obverse there are inscribed – exactly as we would expect if this were a reference to the 'Tripod' – numbers.

Numbers are a prerequisite in many areas, and a great leap forward in architecture was probably a by-product of human communiCation with Cats in Sumer. It must be clear to even a limited intelligence that the architectural arch, developed first in Sumer, is nothing less than the shape

3 Sumerian cuneiform, sa'a, Cat.

---

[21] But see Chatsworth, 'The Cat of unknown name but known face: 'Arramowarra revealed', *JCAT*, Vol. 2, No. iii, pp. 111–16, where it is suggested that it is 'Arramowarra, whom the Sumerians revered as a goddess in her own right.

[22] P. Oiseau, *Sumer sans Oeillères*, Oeuvre et Fermé, Rouen, 1988, p. 85.

[23] For the best argument on this subject, see Rechter, 'Die Katzfrau von Sumer', *KS*, Vol. 2, No. 1, pp. 14–26.

[24] Leichty, *Texts from Cuneiform Sources*, Vol. IV.

[25] I am indebted to Dr Irving Finkel for his grudging concession of the possible validity of this significant construction.

[26] 31 by 31 by 30 cm.

of a Cat's back when she is pleased with a caress or an imminent food offering.

How the unknown architect of ancient Sumer learned that such a shape was strong enough to hold up buildings can, at this early stage of investigation, only be surmised, but there is some evidence that a Cat directly encouraged the construction of the first architectural arch. This is found in an inscription on a mud brick, which has been deciphered as, 'The Cat told me.'[27]

It is not known for certain that the brick formed a part of an arch, but it seems likely that it did. Mud bricks were not an innovation but an established tool at Sumer, and therefore it would be unreasonable to suppose that a Cat would tell a builder to make mud bricks. The phrase could only have referred to some new technological breakthrough. Thus it seems likely that the development of the arch was directly influenced by Cats.

Egypt   The mysterious Twelfth Dynasty Pyramid Text of Pusiris I, found on the west wall of the inner sanctum chamber, was written in hieroglyphics representing a language different from that of all other monument inscriptions. It remained untranslatable after the discovery of the Rosetta Stone.

In 1911, the Egyptologist Belophon suggested that the writing might represent a 'higher' hieroglyphic; that is, that there was another level of the sacred language, which was used by the priests to record the highest magic and protected wisdom.[28] He also, remarkably, suggested that Cats had been worshipped as early as the time of Pusiris, a much earlier date than is commonly accepted.[29] His theory received little acknowledgement at the time,[30] partly because his suggested translation was unreliable.

However, a recent discovery has proved Belophon to have been very much on the right track. This is the present writer's rediscovery[31] of a papyrus originally found in the Eighteenth Dynasty Temple of Myt-Ankh-Amau.

The Myt-Ankh-Amau papyrus, remarkably, proved to be the key that would unlock the secrets of the Pusiris I inscription. In 1986 Horatia Bleat discovered that this papyrus, which is written in hieroglyphic, is in fact a

---

[27] or, 'Built by Burpas', but this has been shown to be unlikely. See Goodboy, *AJCS*, Vol. IX, No. 3, p. 177. This brick disappeared from the Chicago Museum in 1947.

[28] Belophon, *A Survey of Egyptian Texts*, London, 1911, p. 47.

[29] ibid. ,p. 143.

[30] He was hounded out of the profession and died drunk in a cheap Paris hotel (Hôtel Déchirement, 48 Rue Duchien) – not, alas, a rare fate for those whose thinking is ahead of their time!

[31] Under a mummy case in the basement storage of the British Museum.

palimpsest.[32] Another layer of writing was discovered under this writing, a discovery thought to be of little significance until the lower layer was shown to be the same mysterious hieroglyphic as that found in the Pusiris I sanctum chamber. The papyrus is heavily damaged, and only parts of each layer may be read. Nevertheless, the conviction that both layers of the palimpsest recorded the same information[33] allowed the code to be cracked and made the translation of much of the sanctum west wall possible for the first time.[34] This cast a startling new light on Egyptian cultural development.

As Belophon[35] had suggested, the sanctum chamber text did involve 'magic'. Although the text is damaged and has many lacunae, it is apparently nothing more nor less than a treatise on the necessity of and methods for keeping clean the human body![36] Reference is made to secret names, and in particular the names of teachers. The two names that can be deciphered are undoubtedly the 'ineffable', or higher names of Cats.[37]

As is well known, in ancient Egypt, names were of such importance[38] that the world was believed to have been created when the god Khepera or Neb-er-tcher uttered his own name.[39] Egyptian magic held that the knowledge of their names gave one power over gods[40] and demons.[41]

---

[32] See H. Bleat, *A Tentative Deciphering of the Egyptian Cat Texts*, Bellew, London, 1993.

[33] Half of the text is lost from the papyrus.

[34] It seems that the Egyptian recensionist translated from the higher hieroglyphic line by line, writing the new version directly onto the old. Perhaps the higher hieroglyphic had become outmoded, or possibly the information in the document had been 'declassified'.

[35] Who ought to be rehabilitated, with his name restored to the ranks of reputable scholars.

[36] Although it is beyond the scope of this work, it may be said here that there is evidence that all the system of embalming dead bodies came from a misunderstanding of the technical term 'preserve your bodies from dirt'. This gradually disintegrated into 'preserve your (dead) bodies from decay'. Exactly how humans got it so wrong remains a mystery, but the human mentality is such that once the misunderstanding had occurred, it was impossible to undo the mischief. See H. Bleat, op. cit.

[37] Medico, 4.19.96; 14:05. The names cannot be reproduced here. It is a sign of how far the Egyptians were advanced that they were able to use their teachers' ineffable names, and even to write them down.

[38] The names of the god of the underworld, Amen, for example, were as follows: Amen, Re-Iukasa, Na-ari-k or Ka-arei-k, Kasaika, Arethikasathika, Amen-na-an-ka-entek-share or Thek-share-Amen-kerethi, Ireqai, Marqathai, Rerei, Masaqbubu, Thanasa-thanasa, Sharehatha-katha.

[39] Wallis Budge, E.A., *Egyptian Magic*, Kegan, Paul, Trench, Trubner & Co., London, 1901, p. 161.

[40] This must be taken as evidence that the priests believed that 'to know a Cat's name' – which in this context can be taken to mean to study under Cats – gave humans power.

[41] Wallis Budge, op. cit., p. 157. Sir Ernest Wallis Budge was in close contact for many years with Mike, the Cat who 'assisted in keeping the main gate of the British Museum from February 1909 to January 1929. According to a pamphlet published after Mike's death, his mother "was fond of sitting on the desks in the Reading Room, and . . .

Horatia Bleat has convincingly suggested that Egyptian was a tonal language,[42] and the many depictions of musical instruments in their paintings are evidence that the Egyptians valued music. Thus it is clear that cleanliness and names had – with a greater or lesser degree of success! – been introduced to pharaonic Egypt.[43]

---

never hesitated to ask a reader to hold open both folding doors when he [*sic*] wanted to go out into the corridor. Being shut in one of the newspaper rooms one Sunday, and being bored, he amused himself by sharpening his claws on the bindings of the volumes of newspapers, and it must be confessed did much damage. This brought down upon him the wrath of the officials, and he was banished from the library; the Clerk of the Works was ordered to get rid of him, and tried to do so, but failed, for Black Jack had disappeared mysteriously. The truth was that two of the members of the staff arranged for him to be kept in safety in a certain place, and provided him with food and milk.[!] An official report was written to the effect that Black Jack had disappeared, and he was 'presumed dead'; the bindings of the volumes of newspapers were repaired, and the official mind was once more at peace. A few weeks later Black Jack reappeared, and everyone was delighted to see him again; and the chief officials asked no questions!" '

This Cat presented her kitten Mike, at his birth, to Wallis Budge, then the Keeper of Egyptian Cat Mummies of the British Museum, in the spring of 1908. It is with this Cat that Wallis Budge most associated. Mike's obituary verse by F. C. Hiley reads in part,

> So out of all the human crew
> He cared for none – save only two;
> For these he purred, for these he played
> And let himself be stroked, and laid
> Aside his anti-human grudge –
> His owner – and Sir Ernest Budge!
> A master of Egyptian lore
> No doubt Sir Ernest had a store
> Of charms and spells deciphered
> From feline Mummies long since dead,
> And found a way by magic art
> To win that savage feline heart . . .
> Of cats [*sic*], the wisest, oldest, best cat [*sic*]
> This be your motto – Requiescat [*sic*].

Disguised as it is, this may be the first modern description of a Cat teacher and disciple. (see below).

[42] Bleat, H., 'The singing of royal edicts in ancient Egypt', *JRAS*, Vol. 33, No. 6, pp. 196–215.

[43] Mahmoud Assad's contention that the construction of the pyramids is evidence that the Egyptians had attained to the Law of Numbers, however, is wrong. The Cats in Egypt, unlike those in Sumer, had had the sense to keep it back. Unfortunately, it was brought to Egypt from Sumer, early evidence of how volatile the Law of Numbers can be. Modern apologists are quite wrong to suggest that the pyramids had a deep purpose. They are nothing but grandiose testaments of the potentially dangerous action of the Law of Numbers on the human mentality.

The Harappan Civilisation   The presence of Cats in the Harappan cities is indisputable, as skeletal remains have been found.[44] Even without this evidence, however, such a presence could be adduced: as Madhur Alampur points out,[45] the elaborate arrangements for human cleanliness evident in the Great Bath at Mohenjo-Daro in the late third millennium BCE, and the extensive drainage systems, as well as the 'collegiate' structure assumed to be a place of teaching,[46] clearly suggest that Cat mentors were active.[47]

Rechter has suggested that it was at this time that Cats, having recognised the limitations of the human tongue and salivary systems, began to make alternate arrangements for a species that, in this respect at least, was at its evolutionary limit.[48] He believes that from this point water was accepted as a substitute for saliva in the physical cleansing process in humans – a development that remains in common use throughout the human world to this day.[49]

Several Indus Valley seals are also illuminating. A seal bearing the image of a horned tiger[50] and a female figure wearing a horned helmet and

---

[44] 'There is a chance that both the desert cat [*sic*] (Felix Lybica) and the domestic cat [*sic*] (Felix Catus) are present, but confirmation will have to await further comparison.' Victoria Stack Kane, *Animal Remains from Rojdi*, cited in *Harappan Civilisation and Rojdi*, Gregory L. Possehl and M.H. Raval, Oxford and IBH Publishing Co., New Delhi, 1989, p. 183.

[45] Alampur, M., *HarapPaw: Catprints in the Indus Valley*, I to I Press, Regina, 1994, p. 31.

[46] Wheeler, M., *Civilisations of the Indus Valley and Beyond*, London, 1966, p. 13–18.

[47] Alampur, op. cit., p. 15.

[48] It has been suggested by Dogfodder that it was the 'complete cockup in Egypt' – where the elaborate system of perfumes and ointments developed for the purpose had been misunderstood and used instead for the embalming of the dead – that 'forced Cats to overcome their fear of water' ('Cat prejudice meets *force majeure*: a single, cherished example of a cat [*sic*] aboutface', *JCAT*, Vol. 9, No. ii, pp. 188–277). There is no need for his triumphalist attitude. It has long been admitted by Cats that they were too long in overcoming an unwise aversion to water, though it was perhaps understandable in light of the fact that to Cats' highly evolved and sensitive nasal apparatus, most water on the planet stinks dreadfully. It was only natural that Cats thus should overlook its cleansing possibilities. It is not too far from humans being asked to accept that urine has antiseptic properties, which is perfectly true, but how many women would think of bathing their babies in it? Cats feel their mistake. It is completely unnecessary for Dogfodder to rub their noses in it in this way.

[49] In the light of the linguistic evidence from Sumer, above, this theory, although certainly interesting, will have to be revised. It may be that the acceptance of water as a cleansing fluid had come much earlier, and that the difficulties in Egypt arose from a limited experimental attempt to wean humans from water. If so, the experiment, as already discussed, failed. Thus the extensive Indus Valley baths, and those of Minoan Crete, may have been a quick 'containment response' to the damage. Cats were later able to substitute olive oil among the Greeks with more success, and within the present era, of course, sand has been accepted as a substitute in desert countries.

[50] Although, as mentioned above, it was forbidden in most periods and cultures to represent

4 The priestess found at Knossos. One of the few Cats found represented in art outside Egypt from the pre-Cataclysmic period. Note that her skirt has seven tiers, which led to the mistaken placement of the Cat on the priestess's head. (Drawn by Philip Snow)

5 Knossos. Cat on roof of shrine, indiCating that it is the source of the priestess's wisdom. Note that the priestess wears tabby stripes in immitation.
(Drawn by Philip Snow)

possibly a tail is significant. The bowing female, with wide-open arms, appears to be trying to embrace the tiger. This may be a symbolic representation of the human attempt to 'embrace' the 'tiger's' wisdom in ancient Harappa.[51]

The Minoans   Cat influence on the development of the great civilisations of Crete and Thera in the first half of the second millennium is now certain. It is significant that the small votive statue of the 'snake' goddess found at Knossos is accompanied by a Cat.[52] Indeed, Sir Arthur Evans, in his reconstruction, actually placed the Cat on the goddess's head (Fig. 4). There is some reason to believe that in this he was advised by his Cat Snorkles, whose motivation, perhaps, was admirable, but whose scholarship was questionable. It seems likely that a confusion occurred with the seven tiers of the priestess-goddess's skirt, or, as Derek Chatto has humorously suggested, 'perhaps Snorkles chose that inauspicious moment to speak in the Fantasy Voice'![53]

A circular shrine with the image of a goddess or priestess, however, showing on its roof the reclining figure of a Cat (Fig. 5), is certainly authentic. Since the Cat is not in any ordinary posture one might expect of a Cat who was on a roof merely to hunt birds or the like, this clearly indiCates that Cats were considered the highest source of wisdom – i.e. above the roof of the temple.

Very convincing further evidence of Cat influence on the civilisation of Crete is called the 'bathtub proof'. As at Mohenjo-Daro, the presence of so many baths and bathing arrangements, and the sophistiCated plumbing in the great palaces of Minoan Crete, are clear proof that humanity was under the direct tutelage of Cats during this rich period of history. In concert with the Cat statue, the evidence can hardly be interpreted otherwise.

That the teaching of the Law of Cleanliness had such rich results in Crete may be evidence that Cat influence was able to reach deep into every aspect of Minoan culture. It is clear, therefore, that since it is Cats, and not bulls, who led the development, the generally accepted view that

---

the Cat mentor in figurative form, the 'big Cats' were acceptable as a substitute, and therefore all ancient depictions of tigers and lions should be seen as Cats. For the argument see Toadie, 'Thou shalt not make unto thee – following the letter and not the spirit of Cat teachings', *JCAT*, Vol. 3, No. iv, pp. 1208–17.

[51] This motif surfaces again in later cultures where kings are often portrayed 'hunting the lion'. See below.

[52] It is not yet known why the embargo on the representation of Cat mentors in art was violated (or perhaps lifted?) in the Minoan civilisation.

[53] 'Defining "Cat-Headed" in the ancient world', *UBCAT*, II, No. i, p.1.

the decorative shapes seen everywhere on the palace at Knossos are bulls' horns must be mistaken (Fig. 6). It is now suggested that these decorative features are in fact representations of Cats' ears.[54] The impliCation is that the civilisation was 'Cat-headed', that is, led by Cats.[55]

Cat involvement with this civilisation, so brilliant that some experts believe it was the basis for the Atlantis legends,[56] must be taken as proved.

The Hittites   The Hittites, or Hatti, as they called themselves, have left remarkable evidence of their study of Cat wisdom. Lions adorn the gateways not only of the royal palace, but also of the temples in the Hittite capital of Hattusas, and support the throne.

According to David Wright, dogs were not only killed as part of a ritual of purity in this society, but were actively considered evil.[57]

Striking evidence of Cat influence among this ancient people can be found in the sacred language of the Hatti, which was reserved exclusively for ritual use. This Indo-European language, called by scholars Proto-Hittite or Hattian, was the language of priestly recitals in the religious observances. So little remains of such utterances that the language cannot be understood, but one thing is certain: all such passages were preceded by the word 'ḫattili'[58] – 'in Hattian', as Gurney suggests.[59]

It is now suggested, however, that the language called 'Hattian' by scholars may have been the language called in this book 'Cat'. If so, such passages might have been recited in Cat as direct quotations from a Cat

6 Palace at Knossos. The so-called 'bull's horn' decoration is in fact a representation of Cat's ears. After Fanourakis.

[54] But see Bempuss, 'Cross-cultural fertilisation or same-source inspiration? An examination of simultaneous Cat influence,' *AJCS*, Vol. VIII, No. 3, where he points out that many ancient cultures had depictions of tigers and lions wearing horns, and that therefore all depictions of bulls should be taken, like lions and tigers, as a coded representation of 'Cat'. He argues that bulls, lions and even elephants became sacred first as avatars of Cats; later on, this link was forgotten, and the animals were mistakenly worshipped as themselves.

[55] But see Toadie, 'I'm all ears, a new interpretation of Minoan cult objects', *JCAT*, Vol. 10, No. iii, where she argues that the Cat ears signified that the population as a whole was 'Cat-eared', that is, attuned to Cat utterances.

[56] It was not, of course. See below.

[57] 'In the Anniwiyani ritual a gate of *hattalkisna*-wood is erected, a dog is cut into two pieces, and half is placed on each side of the gate. The patients pass through the gate which is then destroyed by the last person going through it. They leave the area of the ritual and "nail down" the road, that is, *fix the evil in its place.*' (italics mine). Wright, *The Disposal of Impurity: Elimination Rites in the Bible and in Hittite and Mesopotamian Literature*, Scholars Press, Atlanta, 1987, p. 35, n.60.

[58] The *ḫ* is 'probably a lost laryngeal' (Gurney). I have suggested elsewhere that it is related to ^, the laryngeal squeak.

[59] O. R. Gurney, *The Hittites*, Penguin, 1990, p.101.

7 Hittite hieroglyphic, **Hatti**. *Sacred Pool of Hattusa.*

teacher. Indeed, the word 'ḫattili' may not mean, 'in Cat' at all, but rather something closer to 'as the Cat said'.[60]

The recently published hieroglyphic inscription at the Sacred Pool of Hattusa offers stunning confirmation of this theory. Here, 'a tall, slender sign with three splayed prongs, the middle one showing a pronounced kink'[61] (Fig. 7) has been shown to be the sign for 'Hatti'. 'What the sign Hatti represents and why it is used to write "Hatti" are unknown.'[62]

The mystery is solved by a simple movement of the sign through 180 degrees.[63] There could hardly be a clearer representation of a tripod![64]

As at Sumer, the resonances inherent in one word are richly symbolic – remarkably so. Thus the word 'Hatti', with its pictographic representation of a tripod, really means something like, 'the Cat people who are led by Tripod wisdom'.[65]

The Americas The Jaguar Cult of the ancient Olmec peoples of North and Central America, traces of which still survive today, have been shown by Amigo de Gata to have originated in a derelict Tabby Cult that resulted from a tragic tenth millennium BCE plague[66] that virtually wiped out Cats in the Americas for a period of several thousand years.[67] Human memory of and longing for the golden age of Cat teaching gave rise to a

8 Late Egyptian hieroglyphic, **Khatti**.

[60] A major adjustment of the dates of the Hittite kingdom, which seems likely in the near future, will not significantly affect the argument. Although, as may soon be agreed, the *main* period of the Hatti kings probably began only in the early first millennium BCE, some knowledge of Cat would certainly have been preserved from the earlier period. In such a case, the fragments called *ḫattili* would have been scarcely understood ritual utterings from ancient times (not unlike Latin in the Catholic church early in this century). In India, for example, remnants of early tripod influence remained as late as the ninth century AD (see below). Nor would their name as 'Cat people' have been given up simply because they were no longer led by Cats. Cf. coinage in the United States, which still bears the legend 'In God we trust.'

[61] J. David Hawkins, *The Hieroglyphic Inscription of the Sacred Pool Complex of Hattusa (SUDBURG)*, Wiesbaden, 1995, p. 33.

[62] ibid., p.25.

[63] Cuneiform went through a similar inverting when the scribes began to hold the tablets at a different angle.

[64] Note that Late Egyptian hieroglyphics also use a reverse three-prong pictograph in their sign for the people they called 'Khatti'. See Fig. 8 and *Non-Verbal Sentence Patterns in Late Egyptian*, Groll, OUP, 1967, p. 51.

[65] This theory also, of course, accounts for the derivation of the word 'Cat', which exists in ancient Greek and Latin and every European language since.

[66] The information in this section has been taken from A. de Gata, 'Origin of the Mayan mysteries', *AJCS*, Vol. IX, No. 11, pp. 415–28.

[67] But note the interesting argument of Vasco de Gata, in *Cataclysmerica*, who argues that this did not occur until 1400 BCE, the time of the Cataclysm (see below).

custom in which certain humans dressed up as spotted tabby Cats to give instruction or comfort to the community. Over time, partly because there were so few Cats in the area and partly because the impersonators were of course larger than the Cats they impersonated, wisdom came to be associated not with Cats but with jaguars. By the time Cats returned to this area in sufficient numbers to make an impact, it was necessary for them to utilise the Jaguar Cult in order to disseminate their wisdom. This gave rise for a time to the curious phenomenon of Cats being forced to dress up as jaguars – in other words, in a distorted image of themselves – in order to dispense teachings.[68]

Insufficient work has so far been done on the impact of Cats in the Americas. It is an area ripe for study.

Cross-cultural Representation of the Tripod

It seems likely that the Cat terms, **rir-rro-mbo,** for Music, Cleanliness and Names, actually gave rise to the word Tripod in some human languages. In ancient Crete, for example, a tablet in Linear B script[69] significantly uses three signs to indiCate the word 'tripod' (**ti-ri-po**)(Fig. 9).[70] The first of these signs, a triangle with a small stick standing upright inside, is read, according to Ventris's decipherment, *ti*. The second, a human figure with what may be a piece of cloth waving beside its head, is read *ri*; the third, an upright stick with a ninety-degree rotated *pi* shape on top, is read, *po*.

It requires no stretch of the imagination to see in the first symbol the musical triangle, nor the close relationship between the Greek *ti* and the Cat **rir**. The second symbol clearly evokes a human figure with a towel around its neck, and the similarity between the Greek *ri* and Cat **rro** needs no belabouring. The third symbol is perhaps less obvious until one remembers the intimate connections between the Law of Names and that of Numbers. In this light, the symbol of *pi* above the stick becomes clear: above the last of the Tripod arts is the mystery of numbers. The Cat **mbo** is as closely related to Greek *po* as is evident in the other two instances.

Thus, the ancient Cretan Linear B word 'tripod' originally may literally have meant, 'Music, Cleanliness, Names'.

This theory casts a powerfully significant light on the so far undeciphered Harappan script and language. On several significant seals, notably seal M-308 from Mohenjo-Daro (Fig. 10), there are three remarkably similar

*9 Linear B, **Tripod**.*

---

[68] 'Only among humans!' as Cats are fond of saying.
[69] Tablet PY Ta641, found at Pylos in 1952.
[70] A. Parpola, *Deciphering the Indus Script*, CUP, 1994, Fig. 34.

signs above the images of a human figure and two Cat (tiger) figures. In this, the stick lies beneath rather than inside the musical triangle, but the similarity can hardly be disputed. The human figure, too, is remarkably like its Cretan counterpart; in other Indus Valley seals the towel is more obvious than here. The third symbol, disappointingly, shows only two upright sticks with a small bar at the base of the right-hand one, as if the top bar of a fully inverted *pi* had come adrift. Whether this symbolises that the Law of Names was not so successfully introduced into the culture can, at this point, only be a matter for conjecture.[71]

Two symbols, larger than the others, remain to be interpreted on the seal: a Y-shape composed of three equal arms with a frill on the right-hand arm, and an H-shape with three crossbars. Since both of these symbols are based on a structure of three,[72] it seems reasonable to suggest that they represent the names of the Cat-like figures who are clearly tutoring the human, perhaps in the dance (symbolising, of course, music).

It is not necessarily being suggested here that the language or writing system of ancient Harappa is intimately connected with Cretan Linear B, but the possibility that the two cultures may have derived their wisdom from a common source should perhaps not be ignored.[73]

10 Harappan seal.
A human figure dancing
with two tigers.
Mohenjo-Daro M-308.
(Drawn by Philip Snow)

The Great Cataclysm

In approximately the year 1450 BCE the first of a series of global natural disasters continuing over several centuries that were to significantly affect human development occurred on earth. Together these disasters constituted a Cataclysm[74] of tragic proportions.[75] Possibly due to the close passage of

---

[71] The curious and so far unexplained 'kink' in the third leg of the Hatti tripod may be significant here. It seems reasonable to suggest that Hatti culture had achieved a certain minimal level of understanding of two of the three tripod arts, but was still deficient in a third. This theory is emphasised by the Hebrew root for Hatti (ח, ת, י) as being one letter 'short' (lamed immediately follows yod in the Hebrew alphabet) of Cat (ל, ת, ח), as if the name Hatti itself preserved the information that the people were not fully developed in the Tripod arts. The defective Harappan 'third leg' would undoubtedly indiCate something very similar. Such a variety of symbols, all so rich and multi-layered in their resonance, may be taken as confirmation of a common source behind the learning of various cultures.

[72] Thus giving the seal as a whole the sacred number total of nine.

[73] Feldmaus has suggested that the Hebrew for tripod, *khatzoubah*, may also be significant, in that the first syllable repeats the Germanic word Cat. This is sheer linguistic gobbledegook.

[74] Cat+a+clysm: to wash over or dash against Cats.

[75] Johnny, 9.9.90; 9:00. This event is still unrecognised by modern geologists, historians, palaeontologists and archaeologists, although some are now approaching the subject obliquely by predicting *future* Cataclysm. Cat mentors must seed such information carefully for fear of putting the scientific mind into denial.

a comet,[76] there was widespread destruction and disruption in the form of earthquakes,[77] tidal waves,[78] floods,[79] landslides,[80] volcanic eruptions,[81] famine[82], and death[83] in all of the great Cat-led civilisations of the Mediterranean – Minoan,[84] Hatti,[85] Babylonian[86] and Egyptian[87] – as well as in Harappa,[88] Mohenjo-Daro,[89] Iran[90], Mexico,[91] Iceland,[92] Greenland,[93] Vancouver Island,[94] Africa[95] and China[96].

Worst of all, noxious gases, possibly from the comet's tail, swept large areas of the earth's surface. These gases, although not actually lethal, had a most unfortunate temporary effect on the higher brain centres of those humans who survived the destruction. The vast majority of humans became tone deaf, and could no longer understand the speech of Cats.[97]

The effect on human society was dreadful. Much of the teaching that had been passed on and absorbed was lost. Individuals as well as entire cultures lost their day-to-day guidance in affairs;[98] after a century or so most had forgotten that Cats had ever had a teaching function.[99] Tragically, they remembered that they had once been guided by *someone,* and this is recorded in documents across many cultures as a loss of contact with the gods.[100] It is recorded many times in the classical accounts that the oracles – for example, at Delphi[101] – were often incomprehensible.[102]

---

[76] cf. Velikovsky, who suggested that an explosion on Jupiter produced a comet that collided with or closely approached earth. Although he omits all mention of Cats, his theory is correct in essentials. He shares with Belophon the distinction of being one who ought to be rehabilitated and his theories examined instead of merely repudiated.

[77] Johnny, op. cit., 9:02	[78] ibid., 9:02.54	[79] ibid., 9:03.3
[80] ibid., 9:03.33	[81] ibid., 9:09.13	[82] ibid., 9:08
[83] ibid., 9:03.40	[84] ibid., 9:05.11	[85] ibid., 9:07
[86] ibid., 9:15	[87] ibid., 10:01	[88] ibid., 9:30
[89] ibid., 10:10	[90] ibid., 9:33	[91] ibid., 10:15.5
[92] ibid., 10:17	[93] Floyd, 29.10.96, 19:04	[94] ibid., 19:04
[95] ibid., 19:04	[96] Johnny, op. cit., 10:15.06	[97] ibid., 11:11
[98] ibid., 11:57	[99] ibid., 12:17	

[100] 'My goddess has failed me and keeps at a distance'; see Lambert, W. G., *Babylonian Wisdom Literature*, Oxford at the Clarendon Press, 1960. The universality of these laments has been noted by Julian Jaynes in *The Origin of Consciousness in the Breakdown of the Bicameral Mind*, Penguin, London, 1990, but he completely misses their significance with regard to Cats.

[101] It may be said here that the name 'Apollo' is a misreading of the name 'Apurr', which was the dynastic name of the sanctuary Cats at Delphi, originally a school. This became confused with the name of the sun god in the post-Cataclysmic period.

[102] Herodotus cites several instances of misunderstanding. See the story of Croesus, Book I.

The Fall from Music[103]

Most human societies were deprived of musical ability for several centuries before this crucial function began slowly to recover. One effect of this temporary disability was to prove disastrous: over the period of musical dysfunction, many human languages lost almost all their musical component,[104] becoming the non-tonal monstrosities that such languages as English and German are today.

Deprived of both the guidance of Cats and the civilising effects of music, human societies began to develop in deviant ways.[105] One of the most deleterious of the results of the rise of non-tonal languages was the development of the entirely phonetic alphabet. Since such a writing system is scarcely adequate to the transcribing of highly tonal languages,[106] the phonetic alphabet effectively locked large parts of humanity into the error, blocking any hope of recovery of the tonal component of language. This single aberration has had prolonged and severe effects for human development.

A second grave result was the loss of status of women during this period. Throughout pre-Cataclysmic times, women were generally more advanced musically and therefore linguistically than men, and therefore it was to women that Cats had spoken.[107] Women, traditionally associated with Cats and Earth, now lost their wisdom and could offer no guidance to a world beset by an angry and terrible Sky God, who in any case traditionally was masculine.

By the time Cats began to try to restore their contact with humans (women also recovered their musical abilities more quickly than men), men had taken over the reins of decision and had instituted the worship and propitiation of the Sky God in many societies around the world. They

---

[103] Most of this section learned from Rufus in a private and profoundly circumlocutious interview with the author, 18–19.10.95; 1600–0300. Detailed footnoting as to time of this section has not been possible, as the tape recorder was dogged by faults.

[104] China and Egypt were the notable exceptions. This was probably due to the effect of global wind movements carrying the gases.

[105] It was during this period that the concept *war* arose. Until this time all disputes had been settled on the Cat model of individual combat. The pattern, still observed by Cats, but unfortunately not by humans, is to attempt first to overwhelm the opponent by insult. Only if no clear winner emerges does the dispute escalate to actual biting and hair-pulling.

[106] As this book shows.

[107] 'Bring my sister! . . . Bring my little one who knows the heart of matters, bring my sister!' *The Dream of Tammuz* (2nd millennium BCE) outlines a probably general attitude to women as being the source of wisdom. Oppenheim, *Dreams in the Ancient Near East*, p. 246.

were deaf to any wisdom spoken by women, who, in association with the Earth Mother, were seen as powerless and vulnerable to masculine violence.

It became a matter of urgent necessity to develop communiCation with the male half of the population, in spite of the fact that only rare male individuals could now learn to understand the speech of Cats.[108]

The focus of teaching thus had to be dramatically altered. Any attempt at further training in Music, Cleanliness or Names was hopeless until musical ability had been restored amongst human males so that they could understand Cat in the first place.[109]

Teaching methods were also sharply different.

Individuals whose brains had more residual musical ability were sought out by various means, and were taught methods to enhance this ability, and ultimately, where possible, the language itself. Such training very often had to be conducted in secret,[110] and men began to pride themselves on their study of 'secret wisdom'.

Whenever (rarely) one of these students attained a sufficient level of comprehension in Cat, he embarked on study of the Tripod, and was instructed to spread what he learned through the civilisation to the degree possible. Now there appeared another unfortunate twist: such wisdom soon began to be called 'messages from the gods', and cults and religions often sprang up around the teachings (see below).[111]

From this time, no civilisation was Cat-led in the same manner as in the past, where whole populations had been, to a greater or lesser extent, obedient to Cat teaching. Individuals who had absorbed and were trying to pass on Cat teaching were faced with great obstacles. They were often ignored, even vilified, by the general population. As is the way with humans, however, many of their names are now revered in the human historical record.

---

[108] It is sometimes estimated that a male capable of spontaneous understanding of Cat could be found, at most, once in a century over the whole earth. In pre-Cataclysmic times, *most* women had been capable of this, and large numbers of men.

[109] This thankless task is called by Cats, 'teaching Kittens to wear fur' a reference to the amount of painstaking licking required to stimulate a new-born's fur growth in the rare instance of a defective birth.

[110] The reasons for this are not clear.

[111] Entirely against the wish of Cats, who have no desire to be thought gods. But there was little that could be done to stop this trend.

141

The Post-Cataclysmic World

The Assyrian Empire   The possibility of permanent tone-deafness in the ruling family of the Assyrians (Tiglath-Pileser and his descendants), and much of the population, has been suggested by Benjamin Nathan in his book *Assyria and Power*.[112]

Tragic evidence of the Assyrian loss of contact with Cats is shown by a sudden shift in the meaning of *shura-anu*, which sometime in the first millennium BCE lost its original meaning, 'Cat',[113] and took on its present meaning, 'evil, malicious'.[114]

Manushat has suggested that the astonishing statues in the British Museum of the 'man-headed lion' from Assurbanipal's reign would have served as warning – whether consciously or unconsciously produced – that this was a culture which rejected Cat wisdom.[115]

That mainstream Assyrian society did reject Cat wisdom is thus unquestionable. Nevertheless, there is some evidence that Cats were active in *secret* training programmes in Assyria throughout the first millennium BCE.

The converse figure of the Assyrian 'Lion-Headed God' is almost too obvious to need explanation. It may have been connected with an initiation cult in which the top rank of attainment was signified by 'lion-headedness'. The Lion-headed God would then have been the tutelary deity of the cult. This may refer to a person who has been taught by Cats and gained Cat wisdom – that is, the teacher of the language class – or it may refer to the student who has progressed to a point where he now understands the language.

That certain Cat teachings did survive in Assyria is made clear by the reliefs at present in the Nimrud Gallery of the British Museum. It has previously been considered that the figures in the water outside the city walls were the bodies of the dead or, for example, 'fugitives crossing a river on inflated skins'.[116] That now seems unlikely; there is more reason to think that these swimming figures are soldiers, bathing even during the rigours of battle.

---

[112] Nathan, *Assyria and Power in the First Millennium BCE*, p. 92. He notes that II Chronicles 29:26–9 records how music was played in the temple at Jerusalem to restore it after Ahaz, a convert to Tiglath-Pileser's religion, was overthrown. The impliCation is that music played no part in Assyrian religious ceremonies.

[113] Leichty, Erle, *Texts from Cuneiform Sources, The Omen Series, Summa Izbu.*

[114] Arabic-English Dictionary.

[115] Manushat, 'Self-Assyrian: A man's head on a Cat's shoulders', *JCAT*, Vol. 4, No. ii, pp. 204–21.

[116] Wallis Budge, *Assyrian Sculptures in the British Museum*, Longmans, 1914, p. 38.

Israel Little information exists in the Assyrian records regarding the Lion Cult, but some evidence may be gleaned from the Bible on a sister-cult in ancient Israel.

That the Hebrews revered Cats is evident from as early as Genesis 49, where Jacob blesses Judah as 'the lion's whelp', gives him the sceptre and makes him lawgiver. The Hebrew *gur*, 'whelp, cub', is an interesting word, appearing only half a dozen times in the Bible, generally in the guise of a creature being carefully raised by a lioness, usually in conjunction with young lions.

It may be that these were terms of initiatory significance in the ancient wisdom system that produced the Lion-Headed God of the Assyrians. The four ranks would then be: cub, young lion, old lion, lioness.[117] This reading of the evidence would suggest that Judah was an initiate in such a secret teaching,[118] and that it was for this reason that he inherited the sceptre.

Like the Sumerian and the Hittite, the Hebrew language gives remarkably compact evidence of early influence from Cats on the ancient Hebrews. The word for Cat, *khatoul*,[119] when each letter is given its number value, adds up to the sacred figure 444. This triple repetition of the number 4[120] is symbolic of a high degree of system, order and rulership. This number in turn breaks down into three letters, which can be regrouped to form *d'moot*, meaning 'form, image'. Thus is secretly encoded in this one word the information that Cat was the form or image through which was gained mastery over learning.

Further evidence that the Hebrew fathers were influenced by Cats is found in the high importance placed on cleanliness. Cleanliness was placed next to godliness in the list of human virtues.

---

[117] The old lion kills for the cubs and the lioness, but it is the lioness who 'brings up' (i.e. teaches) the cubs and young lions. Clearly therefore, it is the lioness who enjoys the highest rank.

[118] Judah was a pre-Cataclysmic king, of course. Nathan believes that the Hebrews had repudiated the wisdom of women at least a millennium before the Cataclysm, perhaps because a grave shortage of Cats in the area meant that women were not, in fact, very wise. It may be that the method of secretly teaching individual men had been adopted by Cats through necessity, and this was later (post-Cataclysmically) viewed as a test case. It is possible that this is where the concept 'chosen people' arose. See Nathan, *Assyria and Power, passim*.

[119] The word first appears in the Midrashic and Talmudic sources, but it may be etymologically related to the Egyptian word *Chaou*, Cat (according to Champfleury) or to the Hittite word *Hatti* (see above).

[120] The number of the Emperor in the Kabbalah and Tarot.

143

Solomon   'Solomon is said to have possessed an ivory throne the six steps[121] of which were flanked by lions, and it had two lions in addition on either side of the seat.'[122]

One of the first acts of King Solomon's reign was his marriage to a princess of Egypt,[123] where Cats had never ceased to be held in the highest esteem; and it is not unreasonable to suppose that the daughter of Pharaoh brought her Cat mentor[124] with her to Israel. It is only *after* this that Solomon 'asks the Lord for wisdom' and is granted it.[125] Subsequently, Solomon designed and built as residence for the daughter of Pharaoh a house that contained a huge bathing pool.[126] It seems reasonable to suggest that Solomon gained his wisdom through study with his wife's teacher. This hypothesis is given weight by Solomon's renowned skill in song.[127]

Persia   From the time of Darius, in the sixth century BCE, representations of lions were very prominent in monumental art.[128] Darius is considered by some modern scholars to have been a usurper, but it is more likely that his right to the throne, instead of deriving from blood descent, may have been derived through attainment of high initiatory rank in a Persian Lion Cult similar to that of the Hebrews and Assyrians. These lion images thus

[121] According to Talmudic legend, the Cat was assigned to the fifth step of the throne. Drach (cited in Clarke, op. cit., p. 317) quite rightly disputes the antiquity of this; Cats must have been *above* Solomon, on the 'eighth level', and therefore would not have appeared at all. Later tradition, in an attempt to maintain the Cat presence, would have mistakenly placed them below, rather than above the lion.

[122] B. Bharatha Iyer, *Animals in Indian Sculpture*, Taraporevala, Bombay, 1977, p. 64, n. 4, citing Gertrude Jones, *Dictionary of Mythology, Folklore and Symbols*, New York, 1961. Note that thus Solomon may have been on the 'seventh level' of any wisdom training; a high level of achievement for those times, but no higher than would be expected of a king renowned far and wide for his wisdom.

[123] I Kings 3:1.

[124] By tradition named Myt.

[125] I Kings, 3:6–15.

[126] ibid., 7:23–6.

[127] It has long been a subject for debate what language Solomon spoke with the Queen of Egypt (Sheba) when she visited him to question him. It is now clear that they certainly *could* have spoken Cat.

[128] It is now clear that many of the reliefs of ancient Persia have previously been misinterpreted. Reliefs in the Hall of a Hundred Columns at Persepolis, for example, previously considered to be a 'hero fighting a lion', and in the Palace of Darius, previously described as 'hero strangling a lion' (Plate I) must be re-examined. The postures of the figures are more consonant with a male figure receiving instruction from a Cat figure, possibly in music and dance, than killing it. The knife then becomes a symbolic Cat's claw, which may have been part of the ritual of passage through one of the ranks in the cult. Indeed, it seems likely that 'Lion-clawed' may have been one of the lower ranks on the way to 'Lion-headedness'. (cf. the Mohenjo-Daro seal, Fig. 10.)

I *Persepolis. Male figure dancing with lion. West jamb of southern doorway of room 5. Palace of Darius. Photo courtesy of Chicago Oriental Institute.*

145

would have been meant as a message to the initiate that (like Judah) his political power derived from Cats (i.e. through being trained in their wisdom).[129] This would account for the some twenty rebellions in the Empire that greeted his ascension to the throne, since most of Darius's subjects would not have understood the message, and might in any case, as mentioned above, have been hostile to Cat wisdom.

Zarathustra Hundliebe points out[130] that Cats are not mentioned in any of Zarathustra's hymns, or *gathas*, either as evil[131] or as good.[132] Nevertheless, he considers them to have been numbered among the 'fierce animals'. In direct contradiction of this, however, we may look at the testimony of Aelian, who mentioned in the second century AD the shrine to the Zoroastrian goddess Anahita, where 'tame lions welcome[d] and fawn[ed] upon those on their way to the shrine'.[133] Hundliebe ignores this evidence entirely.[134]

We must also ask the question why, if Cats were reviled as part of evil creation, Zarathustra's teachings should have so closely reflected those of the Tripod. His *gathas* were sung, and the emphasis he placed on purity and cleanliness may almost be taken as certain evidence of Cat influence.[135]

Further evidence may be adduced from the position of dogs within the religion. Although much has been made of the fact that dogs were used in religious rituals, particularly the ritual purifiCation of the dead, on closer examination this is less convincing as evidence of dogs' sacred position than it might be. In this ritual, a dog was driven three times round a dead

---

[129] It seems likely that the underground Mithraic temples of the ancient Roman Empire, which have so mystified scholars, were simply schoolrooms for the secret teaching of Cat.

[130] Hundliebe, R., *Also Sprach die Katze von Zarathustra Nicht Weil Er Keine Hatte*, Schwein, Berlin, 1993, pp. 442–7.

[131] In the religion inspired by Zarathustra's teachings, all creatures are divided into two Categories: 'Good Creation', from Ahura Mazda, and 'Evil Creation', from Ahriman.

[132] This is highly suggestive. There is no reason for Cats to be omitted – especially from musical composition – unless because, as mentioned above, all mention of Cat mentors in art and writing was forbidden.

[133] Aelian, *On the Nature of Animals*, Loeb Library, Heinemann.

[134] There is also evidence provided by Zoroastrianism in Armenia, where Cats may have been revered 'because they killed mice' (Russell, *Zoroastrianism in Armenia*, Cambridge, Mass., 1987, pp. 459–60). Cats were called 'mouse-killer' both in Armenian and in Sogdian (Gershevich, *A Grammar of Manichean Sogdian*, para. 382, n.1). Mice were unquestionably part of evil creation, because they ate stored grain, and those who killed animals from the evil creation gained in religious virtue in relation to the number of such kills. Thus Cats must have been seen as, at the very least, filled with virtue.

[135] If humanity had only continued to obey his behests, the world and its oceans and air would not be the polluted mess they are today.

body, and, if unwilling, six or nine times.[136] Dead bodies are certain pollution within Zoroastrianism, and it is suggested here that animals forced into the presence of pollution can scarcely themselves be considered unpolluted. Compare the position of the Untouchable caste in India, who similarly were concerned with the disposal of dead bodies.

India   Simhapala has traced the unusual tenacity of Cat teachings in post-Cataclysmic India throughout the Asokan and Mauryan periods,[137] and the surprising, because so late, association of lions with a tripod image (Plate III). Statues of Siva as late as the ninth century still bear the lion-faced crown which calls to mind the 'lion-headed' gods of the ancient Middle East. Simhapala explains the mysterious lion face, *kirttimukha* – 'Face of Glory', which later came to be associated with a myth about a lion-faced monster obedient to Siva, as being a predictable distortion of the original reference to Siva being obedient to the lion, i.e. to Cat wisdom. The further description of 'the fundamental lion face with sinister brows . . . grafting boar's ears, Cat's eyes and buffalo horns mutates into . . . *kirttimukha*'[138] perhaps sheds light on confusions between bull and buffalo horns and Cats' ears in interpretations of sculpture elsewhere, notably in Minoan Crete (Fig. 6 and Plate II). Simhapala also explains the associated word *caitya* as originally meaning 'place where Cat wisdom is taught'.[139]

Simhapala believes that the so-called 'hermit Cat' of the still mysterious Pallava sculpture (Plates V and VI) has been misunderstood in all previous interpretations. 'What has been entirely overlooked by all interpreters is the utterly pivotal position of the Cat within the sculpture as a whole. It is clear to anyone viewing it in its entirety that the Cat (whose strength is, by its close proximity, associated with the elephant) *is holding up the entire structure*. This may well be the manifestation of a deeply buried cultural memory that upon Cat wisdom rests 'all the Law and the Prophets", so to speak'(original italics).[140]

It is curious that, having come so close, Simhapala does not make the final connection: that the Pallava sculpture is a representation of "The Cat Who Holds Up the World', a metaphorical figure from Cat legend, representing the continuing attempts by Cats to teach humans.[141]

11 Caracal Cat. Note the resemblance to the structures on the palace at Knossos (Fig. 6). (Drawn by Philip Snow)

---

[136] Vendidad 8.16.

[137] He suggests that, as in China, the language may have remained tonal after the Cataclysmic period, but the argument is insufficiently defended.

[138] G. Simhapala, *Cat of Nine Tales: Feline Influence on the India Subcontinent from Harappa to the British Invasion*, citing Bharantha, *Animals in Indian Sculpture*, p. 68.

[139] ibid., p. 72.

[140] ibid., p. 130.

[141] See Appendix A.

II *Dogfodder illustrating the 'buffalo horn' argument. But note the similarity to the Cat's ears (Fig. 11).*

III *Stone lion with tripod symbol. India.*

China   The fact that there is no 'Year of the Cat' in Chinese astrology is of enormous significance, since this can only have arisen from a recognition that *all* years belong to Mow. Bempuss suggests, however, that the Cat is represented in the Year of the Tiger.[142] Chinese legend says that the Cat taught the tiger everything it knew except how to climb a tree. This, as well as being literally true,[143] is richly symbolic. 'Climbing a tree' refers to evolutionary development, and the legend signifies that the tiger (like the lion), while perhaps more evolved than other creatures, is still something less than Cat. It may also be a reference to a secret human training system in China, an area that would richly reward investigation.[144]

Confucius   It has long been known that the name 'Confucius' is a misnomer, indeed, not a name but a title. 'Kung' was Confucius's family name. His own first name was 'Qiu', and the name of the philosopher, written in the Chinese style, was simply 'Kung Qiu'. 'Futschu' is a title meaning 'Wise One', 'Seer' and can only be a reference to the Kung resident Cat, whose name was by tradition Foosh – a clear mispronunciation for 'Futschu'.[145] Thus the word 'Confucius' really means, 'the Kung with the Wise One'; a meaning curiously retained by the Latinised form – 'con'[146] or 'with' Fucius.

The Fall from Names

Greece   The fact that one of the representations of the Goddess of Wisdom, Athena, was a Cat is significant to our argument. Athena is generally accepted to have been a pre-Hellenic goddess, and as well as goddess of wisdom, she was considered the source of such arts and handicrafts as spinning and weaving. She was also, most significantly for our argument, the inventor of the flute.[147] The connection is too marked to be unimportant here. Wisdom, music and Cats associated in this way with a goddess indiCates almost beyond the possibility of doubt that Cat teachings were being carried on as late as the Classical period.

---

[142] Bempuss, op. cit., p. 91.

[143] Fluffy, op. cit., 14:02.

[144] Cal, op. cit., 7:11.

[145] Sometimes mistakenly translated into English as 'Sneeze'. This may be more than an interesting coincidence: the ancient Talmudic legend says that the Cat first appeared in the Ark when Noah, in response to popular demand aboard, stroked the back of a lion, who promptly 'sneezed' a Cat out of his nostrils.

[146] *cum.*

[147] *Oxford Companion to Classical Literature*, London, 1969, p.55.

Tragically, however, the human ability to understand Cat was being more and more undermined by the mentally deadening effects of non-tonal human languages. In spite of every attempt to contain the effect, the Fall from Music now led with domino irrevocability to the inevitable next step: the Fall from Names. This is called by humans 'the Birth of Democracy'.[148]

Plato Chateau has argued very convincingly that Plato was a throwback – a rare individual with an almost spontaneous comprehension of Cat.[149] This fact was discovered while he was still a young child by one of the temple Cats serving in the temple of Athena, and Plato was recruited at an early age.

Plato's central mission may well have been to counteract the poison of the new democratic theories and reinject the idea of a moral and intellectual hierarchy into Greek thought. It was hoped that a populace who had accepted the concept of 'philosopher-king' could be more easily led to that of 'philosopher Cat'.

Across the span of history there have been attempts to remind humans of the pre-Cataclysmic Golden Age, as a means of preparing and inspiring them to return to Cat wisdom. The best-known is perhaps Plato's recounting of the story of Atlantis. Later recensionists omit all mention of Cats from this story, including the fact that *Timaeus* was the name of the temple Cat who taught Plato.[150]

The Fall from Cleanliness

Jesus Evidence for an extreme effort on the part of Cats to stave off looming disaster at this time is found in the legend of the Three Wise Men. By tradition, the name of one these Kings of the East was Caspar, meaning 'Bearing or sCattering Treasure'. The treasures presented were gold, frankincense and myrrh, and it is relevant here to remember the Cat litany, used from ancient times for teaching purposes:

---

[148] Little can be said on the subject of the Law of Names at this stage of human development, beyond the fact that, in a true democracy, each individual will have only one level of name. Individuals thus are unaware of the existence of a hierarchy of ability. This renders teaching virtually impossible.

[149] Chateau, P., *Socrate, Homme ou Chatte?*, Oeuvre et Fermé, Rouen, 1989.

[150] Sophy, 5.6.92. Sophy is a direct descendant of Timaeus.

A clean body is its own perfume,[151]
A good name rings golden in the ear,
Music is incense to Mow.

The symbolism of the three gifts is too clear to be mistaken. They were, of course, the Tripod Laws.[152]

But the mission massively backfired. The human misunderstanding and corruption of the Law of Cleanliness that had taken place in Egypt was nothing compared to what occurred now. Although the Romans, feeding on the remnants of Cat wisdom in the civilisations they conquered, if unable to access it directly,[153] 'still took baths',[154] as Cats say, the third stage of decline was now inevitable. This is called by humans 'the rise of Christianity'.

In the first century, Apollonius of Tyana, a holy man,[155] is said to have refused to bathe or comb his hair.[156] This fashion gained such momentum that three centuries later, St Jerome[157] could state explicitly that dirt was holy, thus confirming many saints and religious persons in a predilection for bodily filth.

Music, cleanliness and names were all now lost to large parts of human society.[158]

---

[151] The modern word *myrrh* is derived from a combination of the Cat **mor**(d1) (perfume, incense) and the word for cleanliness **rro**(d4).

[152] See Chateau, *Or, Mor et Oliban: Les Chats de Jésu Christ*, Oeuvre et Fermé, Rouen, 1990 (published in English as *Gold, Frank and Myrrh: The Cats of Christian Wisdom*). *All* of the Cats' names must of course have been Aramaic: Zahab, Mor and Lebanoh. But no blame attaches to Chateau for the error: Cats often issue disinformation around names because of the danger of the Law of Names getting out of hand.

[153] For an account of why Cats were unable to influence the late Roman empire, see Galliana, 'Lead poisoning and the effect on human musical intelligence', *The Lancet*, April, 1993.

[154] An extremely dismissive remark, and not, as on the surface, moderate praise. It is the equivalent of a human saying, of an otherwise hopeless case, 'at least he can wipe his nose with his fingers'.

[155] Curiously, not in the Christian tradition.

[156] Philostrates, *The Life of Apollonius of Tyana*, Loeb Library.

[157] That such a person could be called a saint makes Cats alternately laugh and cry.

[158] This may be an overstatement. A new book casts exciting new light on the 'succession' rock murals of the Sassanians, where Ahura Mazda is seen to be passing the ring of kingship – to the new king, as has previously been believed. The symbolism of this ring has never been satisfactorily explained. Now it is suggested that it is the jewelled collar and ribbon from the neck of the Cat teacher, just deceased. The murals would thus mark, not the death of the old and accession of the new king, but the death of the Cat teacher and the 'granting by Ahura Mazda' of a new Cat teacher to the king. Since Cats could not, of course, be figuratively represented in art, the collar was used to symbolise the Cat.

Thus it may be because the kings continued to receive the benefit of Cat wisdom that the Sassanian empire maintained its cultural supremacy over vast areas of the Middle East and Central Asia virtually until the mid-seventh century AD. (See Peyro-ye Gorbeh, *Gorbegan o Halqeh-i Mulk*, Livres Persepoles, Paris, 1997.)

Arabia   *The writer has voluntarily withdrawn the discussion of Cats in Arabia which caused such unforeseen dismay amongst certain individuals at the Bachgarten Fintz congress. No offence whatsoever — indeed, only compliment — was intended, though much was taken. Cats **approve** of human bathing, especially five times a day.*[159] *It need only be said here that for several centuries Cats hoped that the Tripod Laws had been successfully re-introduced among humans and that full restoration would be possible.*

The Catastrophe[160]

It need hardly be said that remains from the early Mongols show no sign whatsoever of any influence from the Tripod. Chang has shown that Genghis Khan hated Cats.[161]

Indeed, legend says that as a result of some resistance there, and in a fit of rage, Genghis Khan ordered the destruction of every living thing in the holy area of Bamiyan, and that, as a result, even the blades of grass were pulled up.

Even if this story were exaggerated, as modern scholars mistakenly like to think, it could only mean that Cats in the area were wiped out. The tragic proportions of this will be understood when it is explained that for some centuries the caves of Bamiyan had housed a thriving school of Cat.[162]

The 'Last Ditch'

Europe   Forced to abandon the once-promising area that had now become so inhospitable to their teachings, Cats, for the first time since the Cataclysm, turned their attention to Europe. Here they embarked on an onerous task.[163]

It has been suggested that in some as yet undiscovered way, Cat lexicons and grammars compiled at Bamiyan were somehow preserved and

---

[159] It can *surely* cause *no one* any offence to point out that by tradition Mohammad so respected his Cat that once when she lay sleeping against his arm and he was called away, he cut off the sleeve of his robe rather than disturb her. By tradition the name of this Cat was Muezza (cf. the Egyptian *Myt*).

[160] Cat+a+strophe: the accepted derivation of this word is mistaken: it means 'to turn away from Cats'. There is no more tragic word in the English language.

[161] Chang, M. T. K. W., *Knee-Deep in Cat Blood: The Story of Genghis Khan*, Puss-Wa Press, Peking, 1991, p. 1.

[162] For the best presentation of this argument see Bright, 'Cat among the Buddhas', *JCAT*, Vol. 6, No. ii.

[163] Conditions were now worse than at any previous time in history.

transported to Europe; and that it was an attempt by a woman who had read such texts to speak to her resident Cat that inspired the movement.[164]

What is certain is that some Cats came to believe that the prolonged post-Cataclysmic emphasis on training only men had been a mistake. Since women were the natural linguists, they said, more effort should have been put into teaching women in spite of their lost status.[165]

Their students came to be called in human cultures, 'witches'.

The importance of the contribution of such people as the witches is only now beginning to be realised – and it is to be hoped that the influence of Cats on this significant branch of human learning will be increasingly uncovered as Cat itself is better understood.

However, after a brief, tiny resurgence, understanding of the language was entirely lost to the world, when uncounted Cats and their disciples were wiped out in the witch hunts.[166]

To all intents and purposes, Cats no longer influenced human history. The world was in free fall.

The Abandonment of the Task

At this time, the experiment in human development was shut down. It was then that the Cat who had first proposed humans as a possible species for development was posthumously stripped of her names,[167] and ever since she has been known as 'Arramowarra (the Cat whose Name is Unknown).[168]

The Unclean Age

There followed a period so ignorant of the Tripod, so devoid of understanding, that Cats call it by the worst possible Cat epithet:

---

[164] Bright, op. cit., p.17. There is really insufficient evidence for this theory, attractive though it is.

[165] A decision whose influence has led directly to the birth of the women's movement. Cats now accept that they have been slow to realise that there is *no* influence, however mild or beneficial, which will not get out of hand when let loose within the human community.

[166] A reflection of the Cataclysm. Feldmaus has suggested that this repeated human male response to women's association with wisdom and freedom (i.e. Cats) is an unconscious race-memory anger at the original 'betrayal' of humans by Mother Earth, who could not withstand the violence of the Sky God during the Cataclysm. In just such a way, she suggests, boys who watch their mother beaten by their father grow up to beat their own wives out of anger at the mother's weakness.

[167] Johnny, 1.4.89; 3:08.

[168] For the legend of 'Arramowarra, see Part III.

nmah(f 7). Cleanliness was indeed at an all-time low in most areas of the West, names had been reduced so foully that many humans had only one name of any kind,[169] and if music survived, it was in a counter-productively primitive[170] form.

Worse, the Law of Numbers, (which, as we have seen, had unfortunately already been partially introduced both in pre-Cataclysmic Sumer and again more recently),[171] which ought to be rigorously tied to the Tripod Laws, now divorced itself from any restraint and ran amok. This is called by humans 'the Dawn of the Age of Science'.

The Recruitment of Other Species

At this time, dolphins were introduced to the Law of Music, and showed themselves such singularly apt pupils in all the Tripod Arts[172] that Cats have still not decided which species is more likely to be taken on to the next stage of development.[173]

The Descendants of 'Arramowarra

Certain Cats, however, continued to believe in the possibility of human development, and refused to abandon the mission.[174] These Cats, insisting on humanity's potential,[175] placed themselves judiciously within the human community, and even were able to establish some minimal comprehension of Cat among humans.[176]

It is well for humanity that they were so farsighted.

---

[169] Quite appropriately, of course. The tragedy is not in the paucity of names, but in the fact that no human *deserved* more than one.

[170] This has not so far changed.

[171] In Arabia.

[172] Dolphins have the great advantage of living permanently in their cleansing fluid.

[173] A discussion of this is beyond the scope of the present work. See Minna Fishguard, *The Natural Superiority of Dolphins*, Bellew, 1990, where she discusses the choice facing Cats.

[174] Just as certain Cats never undertook the task of human development in the first place. Such Cats have steadfastly refused to believe in the possibility of human progress from earliest days. In typical, human-centric arrogance, these Cats are mistakenly called by humans 'wild', while those who abandoned human congress are called 'feral'. Both terms are offensive to Cats.

[175] Dogfodder's contention that 'Cats ran back to humanity because they were afraid of the water' is entirely unfounded. As noted above, efforts with dolphins are continuing to this day.

[176] Karel Capek, the Czech dramatist, gives an interesting insight into the means adopted by a Cat intent on teaching a human with potential: 'Will someone explain to me why the cat [*sic* throughout] gets excited in a peculiar way, if you whistle to yourself very softly on a high note? I have tried it with English, Italian and German cats; there is no

The Back Fence Wars

For several tragic centuries after the witch hunts, at a period critical in the world's history, when the Law of Numbers was going ever more wildly out of control among humans, the only humans with whom Cats could make clear contact were either mad[177] or poets.[178] Such people, however interesting, were virtually useless to the Cats called 'Arramowarra's Descendants,[179] who were keen to establish links with people calling themselves 'scientists'.[180] In spite of an avowed adoption of what was called the empiric method, no scientist would understand a thing a Cat said.

---

geographical difference among them: if a cat hears you whistling (particularly if you are whistling as high as you can the Barcarolle from the *Tales of Hoffmann* (see Fig. 12)), she begins in a fascinated way to brush against you, jump up on to your knees, sniff with bewilderment at your lips and finally in some sort of amorous excitement she begins to gnaw passionately at your mouth or nose with an expression of voluptuous depravity; after that, of course, you stop, and then she begins to purr hoarsely and industriously like a tiny motor. I have thought about it many times, and to the present day I do not know from what ancient instinct a cat adores whistling . . . Perhaps in those remote and savage ages there lived some feline deities who to their faithful ones whistled with magic charm, but this is merely hypothesis, and the musical enchantment referred to is one of the mysteries of the cat's soul.' (*I Had a Dog and a Cat*, translated by M. and R. Weatherall).

Frances Hodgson Burnett's biography, *The One I Knew Best of All*, reveals the methods a more sensitive woman might experience: 'She had a little cat which always followed her and jumped upon the table when she sat down [to write], curling up in the curve of her left arm. The little cat's name was Dora, and . . . understood that it was assisting in literary efforts . . . The little cat said nothing, but perhaps [*sic*] in some occult feline way she was assisting.'

[177] By newly current human standards. There has been a massive but unrecorded shift in human thinking over the past five hundred years. The mental patterns that used to cause people to be roundly avoided or locked up now run business, institutions and even countries, and vice versa. In short, people who could talk to Cats were considered insane, no matter how intelligent the information they had received.

[178] We await with much interest the forthcoming *Shakespeare's Cat*, in which Pillow examines the impliCations of the fact that a pork-loving theatre Cat, variously called Frankincense and Baconeater, was for many years Shakespeare's closest companion.

[179] Simply because they were powerless to influence the larger community.

[180] They sometimes came frustratingly close. The naturalist Edward Topsell wrote of the Cat in 1607: 'She whurleth with her voice, having as many tunes as turnes, for she hathe one voyce to beg and complain, another to testifie her delight and pleasure, another among her own kind by flattering, by hissing, by puffing, by spitting, insomuch as *some have thought that they have a peculiar intelligible language. . .*' (italics added). Sadly, in spite of great exertions on the part of his Cat Lyon (Fig. 13), Topsell got no further than this. Perhaps partly because, although he clearly enjoyed it, he considered 'playing' with a Cat 'an idle man's pastime'. Topsell, Edward, *Historie of Four-Footed Beastes*, 1607.

Michel de Montaigne, French essayist, was another. 'When I am playing with my

12 A rare portrait of a Cat writing. Murr lived with the German writer Hoffman, and assisted in the writing of at least one of his books. Hoffman was uniquely gifted in his understanding of Cat, but alas, as one of the class of 'poets and madmen', his reporting of Murr's assistance in his work was not believed. In his notes he called Murr his student. But this portrait indiCates the reverse.

In addition, 'Arramowarra's Descendants were roundly mocked and vilified by Cats who were following the Dictum.[181] These Cats had renounced all attempts to teach humans anything beyond the simple ritual offering to Mow of flesh, milk and water. Living in comfort and doing little to earn it, Dictum Cats assuaged their conscience with the newly propounded belief that humans had actually been put on earth to support Cats while Cats taught the dolphin.[182] Cats who did not live within easy reach of the sea thus considered themselves free of all obligation except that of being prepared to respond to a call to go and teach dolphins.

Meanwhile the distortion of the Law of Numbers reached a climax in the first nuclear explosion, and still many Cats did not see the danger. Some Cats believed a few dozen such bombs would actually improve the world[183] through wiping out major centres of human congregation but leaving the minor centres untouched, where Cats tended to be more comfortable anyway.[184] These Cats also argued that there was so little cleansing fluid[185] on the planet still actually capable of being used for cleaning purposes that a reduction in the number of species or individuals requiring cleansing in water would be advantageous to those who were left.

There was, of course, a time when this opinion was actually correct. But humans perversely missed the window of opportunity for a limited nuclear war, which would have wiped out many Northern Hemisphere cities while still leaving large areas of the planet habitable by Cats.

13 Edward Topsell's Cat, drawn by himself. This Cat, Lyon, was one of the group of Cats calling themselves 'Arramowarra's Descendants. Note the frustration in the eyes.

cat [*sic*], who knows but that she regards me more as a plaything than I do her? We amuse each other . . . ' *The Essays of Montaigne* (trs. Trechmann), Oxford University Press, Vol I, p. 444.

[181] This battle is still being waged today, mostly under cover of darkness, all over the world. Even now, there are many Cats who see no virtue in rehabilitating the human race.

[182] This is variously called the 'Chuckwagon' or 'Peter-Paul' theory.

[183] Nevertheless, Dogfodder's suggestion that a Dictum Cat fed parts of the now human-embargoed Law of Numbers to Albert Einstein in a deliberate attempt to wipe out much of the human race is utter nonsense. No such 'feeding' was necessary. Once the Law of Numbers got out of hand, any reasonably intelligent human could have made the leap.

[184] Large cities have a high proportion of apartments, where Cats are often limited to the company of only one or two humans. They find this boring, as well as rendering them of limited use. Cats ideally require to have access to a circle of at least twenty households, each of which provides regular small offerings to Mow, thus helping the Cat to maintain her own, and humanity's, relationship with Mow.

[185] Water.

The Great ConCatenation[186]

It was soon clear that humans had so thwarted higher plans for the world that the whole thing, including every species with any potential for understanding the Tripod, now stood in danger of extinction. This was considered undesirable.

Cats decided to hold an Extraordinary General Meeting. As far as can be ascertained, this meeting, which was held in secret, open-air loCations all over the world through the latter months of 1962,[187] was attended by all those Cats who called themselves 'Arramowarra's Descendants, the Dictum Cats, and even many 'wild' and 'feral' Cats.[188]

It was not an easy meeting. Many of the wild and feral Cats vented their long pent-up fury with the whole misguided human training programme over fifteen thousand years, and of course it was extremely difficult to refute their arguments. The Dictum Cats accused 'Arramowarra's Descendants of interference in a programme that would have rid the world of its most troublesome species. 'Arramowarra's Descendants, for their part, vilified the individual they rudely called 'Einstein's Cat' (Plate 4) for supposed deliberate leaks of classified information.

At last, however, it was agreed by almost all[189] that the situation must be reversed, by any means possible. This meant an all-out effort on the part of all Cats[190] worldwide to establish widespread new contact with humans by any means, and urgent reintroduction of the Tripod Arts wherever possible, with the ultimate goal of reconnecting the now wildly askew Law of Numbers to these Laws.

The RestorCation

The present writer was fortunate enough to be raised with Cats from birth, and to be often alone with them. That Cats had a comprehensible language

---

[186] 'A coming together of the Cats of all nations.'

[187] Not all Cats attending at all times, of course. Most Cats attended for no more than a few hours or days, but in a way peculiar to Cats, the arguments of the entire conCatenation were afterwards disseminated to all.

[188] The extreme urgency of the conCatenation accounts for the high number of reported 'missing Cats' during this period, most of whom returned to their homes. There were also several unexplained disasters during these months in various parts of the world, such as electrical failures and heavier-than-usual precipitation, all designed to allow Cats to escape restrictive environments undetected. (Johnny, 9.9.90; time unrecorded).

[189] Including most of those who had once imagined that humanity, left to itself, would destroy no one but ourselves.

[190] Many 'wild' and 'feral' Cats would still have nothing to do with the project, and some Dictum Cats, it must be said, are so enfeebled by what is called 'the Mow life', that they take little if any part.

was first suggested to her by her maternal grandmother, who understood such basic expressions as **mRaow**, 'food', and **mupRup mawrow**(b6) **bra**(c4), 'please open the door'.

But it was not until the arrival in 1964 of the significantly named Medico, a Siamese of superCat tolerance, patience and forbearance, that she began to break through the difficult barrier that tonality presented to understanding. It is now clear that the writer and her grandmother were not alone, but were part of this emergency programme that involved choosing suitable people to be tutored by resident Cats.

The publiCation of *The Begin Note's Role in Meaning* in 1982 opened the way to the many others who had been struggling in the field, and from that time humanity has made enormous strides in regaining our ancient connections with Cat wisdom. Numerous books and scholarly papers have been written in the last decade, and the School of Cat Studies was founded in 1988. The first forty students gained a BA(Cat) in 1992. The school now has an annual intake of 280 undergraduate students. The degree of MCat was instituted in 1993. The Royal Cat As Tutor Society (Royal CATS) was founded in 1986, and its magazine, *Journal of Cat As Tutor*, débuted that same year. It is published four times a year.

The Future

Throughout much of human history, humanity was capable of communiCation with, and was guided by, Cats, and it is clear that humanity benefited enormously from the contact. It may not be an exaggeration to say that most of the great leaps forward in human learning can be directly traced to the influence of Cats, through human comprehension of Cat.

The tragic loss of that connection has led directly to the dilemma facing the world today. But through new understanding of, and obedience to, Cat wisdom, we have the chance to snatch the brand from the burning and restore ourselves and, incidentally, the entire earth to health.

IV *Einstein's Cat*

Appendix A

'THE CAT WHO HOLDS UP THE WORLD'

On 15 December 1898, a Miss Dora Chatreuse presented the following translation of a cuneiform tablet[1] to the Society of Amateur Assyriologists.[2] In 1899 the translation was published in the Society's journal. It received little attention, all of it contemptuous, but there was a remarkable absence of other scholars rushing to provide the more accurate translation they insisted was possible. The tablet itself disappeared; the translation has not been seen again until now. For the purposes of this book, a reconstruction of the tablet has been made by scholars, and is reproduced on the cover.

Miss Chatreuse could never have seen the Pallava sculpture (Plates 5 and 6); had she been privileged to do so, it is certain that she would have been impressed by the coincidence between the words and the image in two cultures so separated by time and distance as ancient Sumer and the India of the present era.

Her translation reads as follows:

The Cat Who Holds up the World

> The heaven is fallen
> The earth is [fallen]
> I am th[e Cat] who holds up the world
> The [sun has] gone dark
> The moon has not come out
> [I am the Cat whose] Eye brightens the darkness
> (. . .)
> [The] seas boil (?)
> The land me[lts]

[1] The tablet itself had been published by Professor Georg Andreas in 1896.
[2] It must be more than coincidence that the acronym spells out the phonetic rendering of Sumerian *sa'a*, Cat. Many of the records of this Society have been mysteriously 'lost'.

[I] am [the Cat whose] piss is cold
The waters rise
The mountains [fall]
(. . .) who is (. . .)
The earth shakes
The seas tremble
I am the Cat whose foot is set straight
(. . .)
[I am the] fleet-footed Cat
(. . .)
[I am the Cat who ga]ve power to the Elephant
[I am the Cat who] gave the Lion roaring
[I] a[m the Ca]t who gave the Wild Bull might
[I] am [the C]at who whispered wisdom to the wrongdoer[3]
To give and to take away [are] mine
I am the Cat [who holds up the world]

Transliteration

[a]n ba.šub ki ba.[šub]
[sa].‹a› ki gùr.ru me.[en]
[ᵈutu ba].šú.šú iti$_x$ nu.‹è›
[sa].‹a› igi.bi kukku ‹zálag.ga› me.e[n]
[a.a]b.ba ì.lù ki ì.z[al]   5
[sa.a] kàš.bi še$_4$ m[e.en]
a mu.ìl kur [mu.šub?]
[x x] lú [(x x x)].àm
ki ì.túb.bu a.ab.ba ì.sùḫ
sa.a ‹gìr.bi› si.sá me.en   10
[(. . .)]
[sa].‹a› gìr.bi ul$_4$ sá.sá [me.en]
[(. . .)]
[sa.a] am.si.ra á.kalag.ni mu.na.an.sum.m[a me.en]
[sa.a] ur.mah.ra KA×ŠID.gi$_4$.gi$_4$.ni mu.na.an.sum.[ma me.en]
[sa].‹a› am.ra nè.ni mu.na.an.sum.ma m[e.en]   16
[sa].a lú.nam.tag.ga.ra géštu mu.na.an.‹sum?.ma?› m[e.en]
[sa.a?] me.en sum.mu kar.ra gá.a.[kam]
[. . .] sa.a.me.en [ki gùr.ru me.en'?]

³ i.e. human

V *Mahabalipuram, India. The Pallava sculpture. A late Indian rendering of 'The Cat Who Holds up the World'. Photo courtesy the American Institute of Indian Studies, Varanasi.*

VI *Mahabalipuram. The Pallava sculpture. Detail. Photo courtesy Donald M. Stadtner.*

Appendix B

TRANSLATIONS

CHAPTER ONE

The Cat. The Cat is pretty. You (C) are hungry. The food is cold. The whiskers are wet.

CHAPTER TWO

Milk is nice. Wet fur is not nice. The little Cat has a small tail. You (nC) must make an offering of milk (to Mow).

CHAPTER THREE

Your food is in the bowl. The salmon is swimming in the water. I (C) want food. At night the Cat hunted and in the morning she played a trick and laughed.

CHAPTER FOUR

You really are a very pretty Cat. You (C) have a discerning eye and you saw the mice. Was the mouse's tail specially delicious? It was certainly tasty.

CHAPTER FIVE

You are at rest on my lap. You have been decorating the bathroom. Now you are kneading my knee. Meanwhile I am stroking your fur. You are going to commune with heaven (go to sleep).

CHAPTER SIX

Are you a white Cat without markings? You (nC) must use your eyes better. I am a white Cat with blue eyes and six black hairs on my occiput. The adorable kittens are asleep in the basket. Here is a toy.

CHAPTER SEVEN

Does non-Cat (do you) believe that a Cat's whisker is lucky? I'm sorry, I (nC) didn't quite catch that. There is a canary eating from your dish (joke)! Although it is raining, the Cats are debating in the garden. It was a dark and stormy night.

This child is stupid. The Cat has delivered three Early Warnings. Now the Cat is speaking in Second Maow. The (adult) human is not listening. Does the human have ears? Oh, yes, the human has ears. What a pity it does not use them.

CHAPTER NINE

Mules are better than humans. They only say one thing and no one understands it. Humans say anything they like and then try to shift the blame. Mow has given Cats an onerous task but they undertake it with cheerful determination. Poor humans! They have no tail, no whiskers, and flat ears. No wonder they offend Cats all day long.

Bibliography

Aelian, *On the Nature of Animals*, Loeb Library, Heinemann, London, 1911

Alampur, M., *HarapPaw: Catprints in the Indus Valley*, I to I Press, Regina, 1994

Allchin, B.& R., *The Rise of Civilisation in India and Pakistan*, CUP, 1982

Allchin, F. R., *The Archaeology of Early Historic South Asia*, CUP, 1995

Artemidorus Daldianus, *The Interpretation of Dreams*, Noyes Press, Park Ridge, NJ, 1992

Belophon, Viscount Sir Harry A., *A Survey of Egyptian Texts*, Fearless Press, London, 1911

Bempuss, J., *Cross-Cultural Fertilisation or Same-Source Inspiration? An Argument for Simultaneity in Cat Teaching*, Bellew, London, 1993

Bird, Yami, *Sumer sans Oeillères*, Oeuvre et Fermé, Rouen, 1988

Bleat, H., *A Tentative Deciphering of the Egyptian Cat Texts,* Bellew, London, 1993

Budge, E. A. W., *Egyptian Magic*, Dover, 1971

Chateau, *Or, Mor et Olibanum: Les Chattes de Jésu Christ*, Oeuvre et Férme, Rouen, 1990

de Gata, Vasco, *Cataclysmerica*, Beanbrane Press, Los Angeles, 1996

Fishguard, Minna, *The Natural Superiority of Dolphins*, Bellew, London, 1990

Geotze, Albrecht, *Old Babylonian Omen Texts*, YUP, New Haven, 1947

Gershevich, *A Grammar of Manichean Sogdian*

Ghirshman, Roman, *Iran, Parthians and Sassanians*, London, Thames & Hudson, 1962

Ghirshman, Roman, *Persia, from the Origins to Alexander the Great*, London, Thames & Hudson, 1964

Goold, G. P. and Pope, M., *Preliminary Investigations into the Cretan Linear A Script*, University of Cape Town, 1955

Gorbeh, Peyro-ye, *Gorbegan o Halqeh-i Mulk*, Livres Persepoles, Paris, 1990

Groll, Sarah I., *Non-Verbal Sentence Patterns in Late Egyptian*, OUP, London, 1967

Guimet, *Les Cités Oubliées de l'Indus*, Archéologie du Pakistan, 1989

Hawkins, David J., *The Hieroglyphic Inscription of the Sacred Pool Complex of Hattusa (SUDBURG)*, Wiesbaden, Harrassowitz Verlag, 1995

Hundliebe, R., *Also Sprach die Katze von Zarathustra Nicht*, Schwein, Berlin, 1993

Iyer, B. Bharantha, *Animals in Indian Sculpture*, Taraporevala, Bombay, 1977

Jaynes, Julian, *The Origin of Consciousness in the Breakdown of the Bicameral Mind*, Penguin, London, 1990

Kramer, Samuel Noah, *History Begins at Sumer*, Thames & Hudson, London, 1956

Kramer, Samuel Noah, *From the Tablets of Sumer*, Falcon's Wing Press, Indian Hills, Colo, 1956

Lambert, W. G., *Babylonian Wisdom Literature*, Oxford at the Clarendon Press, 1960

Leichty, Erle, *Texts from Cuneiform Sources, The Omen Series, Summa Izbu*, Vol IV, Locust Valley, NY, J. J. Augustin, 1970

Montaigne, Michel de, *The Essays of Montaigne*, (trans. E. J. Trechmann), OUP, London

Nathan, *Assyria and Power in the First Millennium BCE*, Hashofet Press, Jerusalem, 1994

Oppenheim, Leo, *The Interpretation of Dreams in the Ancient Near East*, Philadelphia, American Philosophical Society, 1956

Oppenheim, Leo, *The Assyrian Dictionary*, The Oriental Institute, Chicago, 1961

Parpola, Asko, *Deciphering the Indus Script*, CUP, 1994

Parrot, André, *Sumer*, London, Thames & Hudson, 1960

Philostrates, *The Life of Apollonius of Tyana*, Loeb Library, Heinemann, London, 1912

Possehl, Gregory, and Raval, M. H., *Harappan Civilisation and Rojdi*, Oxford and IBH Publishing, New Delhi, 1989

Rajeswari, D. R., *The Pallava Sculpture*, Intellectual Publishing House, New Delhi

Russell, *Zoroastrianism in Armenia*, Cambridge, Mass., 1987

Simhapala, G., *Cat of Nine Tales: Feline Influence on the India Subcontinent from Harappa to the British Invasion*, I to I Press, Regina, 1991

Sivaramamurti, C., *Birds and Animals in Indian Sculpture*, National Museum, New Delhi, 1974

Topsell, Edward, *Historie of Four-Footed Beastes*, 1607

Velikovsky, I., *Worlds in Collision*, Victor Gollancz, London, 1950

Wallis Budge, E.A., *Egyptian Magic*, Kegan Paul, Trench, Trubner & Co., London, 1901

Wallis Budge, *Assyrian Sculptures in the British Museum*, Longmans, 1968

Wheeler, Sir Mortimer, *Civilisations of the Indus Valley and Beyond*, London, Thames & Hudson, 1966

Wright, David P., *The Disposal of Impurity: Elimination Rites in the Bible and in Hittite and Mesopotamian Literature*, Scholars Press, Atlanta, 1987

Lexicon

CAT–ENGLISH

'a(a7)	if
'aa(c7)	on, in
'aow(b1)	little, small; flat, not pointed (of ears)
'arra(a7)	question signifier
'aw(c4)(nC)	to continue a displeasing act
'awaruh(f3)	sin, crime, mistake, error
'Rowow(d2)	pretty
'RRaow(a2)	lonely
^ra`(b1)	toy
a`bRah(b1)	bathroom
aaa`(c4)(nC)	to squeak, say
arp(b4, c4)	to run, scurry
arruh(a5)	future, the future
aw(c3)	paw, foot, hand
awa(f 7)	dog
berah(a1, f 7)	to like
b'row(d1) **uh b'row**	'hairs of', i.e. many, numerous, uncountable
b'row(d1)	hair
birr(b5)	milk
birr(b5) **birr**	cream
bra(c4)(nC)	to work; lift, carry, fetch; do
braa`(f 7)(nC)	to sit
brap(b4, c4)	to eat
breh(b4)	tree
broh(a4)	eye
broh(b4, c4)	to see
broh prip(b4)(C)	to look for, to seek
broh pirp(c4)(nC)	to look for, to seek
broh(b4) **uh nbroh** (b4)(C)	to 'look and not look'; i.e. to blink at
brroh(a1)	admiringly, in admiration
brroh(d4)	shadow

168

bRRow(a1, f 7)	to laugh
bRRow(a6)	joke, trick
bRRow(b4)(C)	to play tricks
bRuh(b4, c4)	to wish, desire, need, want
frah(d4)	dark, black
fru(a7)	accordingly, so, thus, as
iow(a7)	or, otherwise; alternatively
iow(f4)(nC)	skin; trousers, clothes
irr(a5)	delicious
m'aaw(b4)(C)	to fight, to engage in (noble) battle; to wrestle; to fight playfully or in a spirit of sportsmanship
m'ow(b2)	softly, gently
m'ow(d1)	dinner, meal
m`	to, for, at, from, off, etc.
m`mow(a1) **mow**(d4) **broh pirp**	to apologise
ma` RRow(a1)(nC)	thank you
ma`row(b3)	coat/fur
ma`uh(f 7)	corrupt, vulgar; human
maa`row(f 7)(nC)	to sing
maaa(a4)	floor
maaow(b4, c4)	to place, put
maaw(d4)(C)	task, divinely assigned duty/responsibility
maaw(f 7)(nC)	job, work, activity
mah(b4, c4)	to leave, depart; vaCate
mah(f 7)	really, quite; an expression of marginal interest or response to unsolicited information
maor(a5)	artist's material; paper; toilet paper
maow(b4, c4)	to come, walk, move forward
maow(a7) **miaow**(b4)	to speak in Second Maow
maow(c7) **miaow**(b4)	to speak in Fifth Maow
maow(d4)	song
maowr(a2, a4)	salmon (flesh)
maowro(b4)(C)	to sing
marr(a5)	canary; bird with strong, interesting odour
marro(a5)	thing, object, idea, place
mawrow(b6)	door
mboh(c5)	big
mbruh(b5)	nice, pleasant
mbruuh(a5)	pleased
mbruuh(d1, a1)(C)	to be pleased with, to approve
me`a(a7)	first; now
meow(b4, c4)	to understand, accept

169

meow(d1)	today
meow(d4)	good, sharp, clear
merah(b1)	house
merowwap(a1, f 7)	to be hungry
meuh`a(a7)	second; then; afterwards; meanwhile; while
meuh(d4)	numbers
mew(b4)(C)	to decorate, rearrange, sculpt; to pull
mew(a4)	(in the) morning
mew(b1)	good
mew(c1)	cold
mew(d4)	night, at night
mew(d4) **m'mew**(a4)	for a long time, 'from night till morning'
mi'ao(a4)	garden
miaow(b4)(C)	to talk, say
mieh(d1)	delicate, dainty, refined; delicately, etc.
miew(a2, a4)	tuna (flesh)
miow(b4, c4)	to think, imagine, dream
miow(E1)	fantasy, imagining, thought
mir(d1)	claw, claws
mirr(c4)(nC)	to purchase, bring for approval, buy
moh(a5)	yes; indeed?
moh(a5) **row**(a1, f 7)	to believe (be in a state of belief)
mor(d1)	perfume, incense
morh(b4, c 4)	to bite
mow(a1) **mbruuh**(a1)(C)	thank you
mow(a1)	Cat, Cat Presence, Higher Being
mow(b4)(C)	to accept an offering to Mow; to eat
mow(b3)	good
mowrow(c4)	winning, lucky
mowruh(a3)	good, well-behaved, wise
mowruh(a5)	secret; secretly; Catlike
mowruh(b4)	quick, fast, quickly; Catlike
mowruh(d1)	majestic; majestically; Catlike
mra'(b4)(C)	to continue, carry on; carry out (usu. ritual)
mRaow(b3)	food
mRaow(c4)(nC)	to walk, move
mraow(b4, c4)	to hunt
mrow(d1, b4)(C)	do, take, make
mRRah(a3)	money
mRRah(a4)	titbit, snack
mRRaow(a3)	testicles
mRReh(a3)	face
mrrew(f 7)	name (nC)

mRRow(b4)(C)	to sleep, to commune with Mow
mrrrow(d4)	anger, displeasure; sorrowful anger
mrrrow(f4)	remorse, regret, sorrow
mrruh(d3)	name (C)
muah(c3)	ticket
muh(a7)	when, nevertheless, and, but, however, who, which, etc.; the subordinate connector
mut(b7)(C)	pay attention!, listen up!
nmbruh(f 7)	unpleasant
nme(a2)	nothing, zero, less than one; fraction
nmow(a1)	no one, nobody
nr'mow(a1)	there
nrow(c4) **rrow**(b3)(nC)	'to have no whiskers', to be stupid, to beg pardon for not hearing
owuh(c4)(nC)	to pull, squeeze, cause irritation to
pirp(c4)(nC)	to bring; offer, make an offering to
pra(c7)	already
pra^(b7)	sofa, firm claw sharpener
praow(c4)(nC)	to swim
preh(c1)	quickly, hastily
prih(b4, c4)	to hear
prih(d2)	ear
prip(b4)(C)	to give, bestow, vouchsafe; to accept, approve
prrew(a2, a4)	mouse(meat)
prruh(b4)(C)	to rest, recline, to grace, to be at ease
pwah(a1)(C)	to dislike, disdain
pwah(c3)	wet
pwah(f 7)	water
r'mow(a1)	here
rir(d4)	music
rir nrow(b4, c4)	to be ashamed
row(a1, f 7)	to be
Row(a4)	bowl, dish
row(b4, c4)	to have
Row^(b1)	lap, knee
rowb maar(b4, d1)(C)	to be angry, to storm, to lash one's tail
rowb(b6)	tail
rrah(c4)(nC)	to work, do
rro(b4, c4)	to wash, clean
rro(d4)	cleanliness
rrobra(c4)(nC)	to lick; to clean with water or other substance
rromiaow(b4)(C)	to lick, to clean with the tongue
RRooww(a1, d1) (C)	to purr

171

RRow(c6)	oversight, error; My Goodness! or What a pity!
rrow(b4)	whiskers
RRow(f 7)	poor, sad, pitiful
RRow(d1, a1)	to bless
RRuh(a5)	virtuous
rrup	'invitation to intimacy'
ruh(a1, f 7)	to intend, mean
ruh(a7)	like, similar to
ruh(b2)	with, by means of
Rup(c4)(nC)	to stroke, worship through caress
trrow(b1)	curtains, ladder, soft claw sharpener
truh(b4, c4)	to stir, mix, prepare; improve upon, adjust, knead, decorate; scratch; sharpen
uh(a7)	and, also
uh(f 7)	but
urr(b4, c4)	to choose
urrt(f 7)	child, offspring, cub (nC)
waa`(c4)(nC)	to scrap, squabble, wrangle
wah(d1)	handsome

ENGLISH–CAT

accept an offering to Mow; to eat (C) *v.*	**mow**(b4)
accordingly, so, thus, as *a.*	**fru**(a7)
admiringly, in admiration *a.*	**brroh**(a1)
already *a.*	**pra**(c7)
and, also	**uh**(a7)
anger, displeasure; sorrowful anger *n.*	**mrrrow**(d4)
apologise (nC) *v.*	**m`mow**(a1) **mow**(d4) **broh pirp**(c4)
artist's material; paper; toilet paper *n.*	**maor**(a5)
bathroom *n.*	**a`bRah**(b1)
be *v.*	**row**(a1)(f 7)
be pleased with, approve (C) *v.*	**mbruuh**(d1)(a1)
be angry, to storm, to lash one's tail (C) *v.*	**rowb maar**(b4, d1)
be ashamed *v.*	**rir nrow**(b4, c4)
believe (be in a state of belief) (C) *v.*	**moh**(a5) **row**(a1, f 7)
big *a.*	**mboh**(c5)
bite *v.*	**morh**(b4, c4)
black, dark *a.*	**frah**(d4)
blink at, forgive (C) *v.*	**broh**(b4) **uh nbroh**(b4)
bowl, dish *n.*	**Row**(a4)
bring; offer, make an offering to (nC) *v.*	**pirp**(c4)

canary; bird *n.*	**marr**(a5)
Cat, Cat Presence, Higher Being	**mow**(a1)
child, offspring, cub (nC) *n.*	**urrt**(f 7)
choose *v.*	**urr**(b4, c4)
claw, claws *n.*	**mir**(d1)
cleanliness *n.*	**rro**(d4)
coat, fur *n.*	**ma`row**(b3)
cold *a.*	**mew**(c1)
come, walk, move forward *v.*	**maow**(b4, c4)
continue, carry on, carry out (usu. ritual)(C) *v.*	**mra'**(b4)
continue a displeasing act (nC) *v.*	**'aw**(c4)
corrupt, vulgar	**ma`uh**(f 7)
cream *n.*	**birr**(b5)**birr**(b5)
crime *n.*	**'awaruh**(f3)
curtains, ladder, soft claw sharpener *n.*	**trrow**(b1)
decorate, rearrange, sculpt; pull (C) *v.*	**mew**(b4)
delicate, dainty, refined; delicately *a.*	**mieh**(d1)
delicious *a.*	**irr**(a5)
dinner, meal *n.*	**m'ow**(d1)
dislike, disdain (C) *v.*	**pwah**(a1)
do, take, make (C)*v.*	**mrow**(d1, b4)
do (nC) *v.*	**bra**(c4)
dog *n.*	**awa**(f 7)
door *n.*	**mawrow**(b6)
ear *n.*	**prih**(d2)
eat *v.*	**brap**(b4, c4)
eye *n.*	**broh**(a4)
face *n.*	**mRReh**(a3)
fantasy, imagining, thought *n.*	**miow**(E1)
fight, engage in (noble) battle; wrestle; fight playfully (C) *v.*	**m'aaw**(b4)
first, now *a.*	**me`a**(a7)
flat, not pointed (of ears) *a.*	**'aow**(b1)
floor *n.*	**maaa**(a4)
food *n.*	**mRaow**(b3)
for a long time *a.*	**mew**(d4) **m`mew**(a4)
fraction *n.*	**nme**(a2)
future, the future *n.*	**arruh**(a5)
garden *n.*	**mi'ao**(a4)
give, bestow, vouchsafe; to accept, approve (C)*v.*	**prip**(c4)
good, well-behaved, wise *a.*	**mowruh**(a3)
good *a.*	**mew**(b1)
good *a.*	**mow**(b3)
good, sharp, clear *a.*	**meow**(d4)
hair *n.*	**b'row**(d1)

handsome *a.*	**wah**(d1)
have *v.*	**row**(b4, c4)
hear *v.*	**prih**(b4, c4)
here	**r'mow**(a1)
house *n.*	**merah**(b4)
hunger, be hungry *v.*	**merowwap**(a1, f 7)
hunt *v.*	**mraow**(b4, c4)
if	**'a**(a7)
intend, mean *v.*	**ruh**(a1, f 7)
invitation to intimacy	**rrup**
job, work, activity (nC) *n.*	**maaw**(f 7)
joke, trick *n.*	**bRRow**(a6)
lap, knee *n.*	**Row^**(b1)
laugh *v.*	**bRRow**(a1, f 7)
leave, depart; vaCate *v.*	**mah**(b4, c4)
lick, to clean with the tongue (C) *v.*	**rromiaow**(b4)
lick; to clean with water or other substance (nC) *v.*	**rrobra**(c4)
lift, carry, fetch (nC) *v.*	**bra**(c4)
like, similar to *a.*	**ruh**(a7)
like (C) *v.*	**berah**(a1, f 7)
little, small *a.*	**'aow**(b1);
lonely *a.*	**'RRaow**(a2)
look for, seek (C) *v.*	**broh prip**(b4)
look for, seek (nC) *v.*	**broh pirp**(c4)
majestic; majestically; Catlike *a.*	**mowruh**(d1)
many, numerous *a.*	**b'row**(d1) **uh b'row**
milk *n.*	**birr**(b5)
mistake, error *n.*	**'awaruh**(f3)
money *n.*	**mRRah**(a3)
morning, in the morning *a.*	**mew**(a4)
mouse (meat) *n.*	**prrew**(a2, a4)
music *n.*	**rir**(d4)
name (nC) *n.*	**mrrew**(f 7)
name (C) *n.*	**mrruh**(d3)
nice, pleasant *a.*	**mbruh**(b5)
night, at night *a.*	**mew**(d4)
no one, nobody (C) *n.*	**nmow**(a1)
nothing, zero, less than one *n.*	**nme**(a2)
numbers *n.*	**meuh**(d4)
on, in	**'aa**(c7)
open *v.*	**bra**(c4)
or, otherwise: alternatively	**iow**(a7)
oversight, error; My Goodness! or What a pity!	**RRow**(c6)
paw, foot, hand *n.*	**aw**(c3)

pay attention!, listen up!	mut(b7)(C)
perfume, incense *n.*	mor(d1)
place, put *v.*	maaow(b4, c4)
play tricks (C) *v.*	bRRow(b4)(C)
pleased *a.*	mbruuh(a5)
poor, sad, pitiful *a.*	RRow(f 7)
pretty *a.*	'Rowow(d2)
pull, squeeze, cause irritation to (nC) *v.*	owuh(c4)
purchase, bring for approval, buy (nC) *v.*	mirr(c4)
purr (C) *v.*	RRooww(a1, d1)
quick, fast, quickly; Catlike *a.*	mowruh(b4)
quickly, hastily	preh(c1)
really, quite	mah(f 7)
remorse, regret, sorrow *n.*	mrrrow(f4)
rest, recline, to grace, to be at ease (C) *v.*	prruh(b4)
run, scurry *v.*	arp(b4, c4)
salmon (fish) *n.*	maowr(a2)
salmon (meat) *n.*	maowr(a4)
scrap, squabble, wrangle (nC) *v.*	waa`(c4)
second; then; afterwards; meanwhile; while *a.*	meuh`a
secret; secretly; Catlike *a.*	mowruh(a5)
see (C) *v.*	broh(a1)
see (nC) *v.*	broh pirp(c4)
shadow *n.*	brroh(d4)
sin *n.*	'awaruh(f3)
sing (C) *v.*	maowro(b4)
sing (nC) *v.*	maa`row(f 7)
sit (nC) *v.*	braa`(f 7)
skin, clothes (nC) *n.*	^ow(f4)
sleep, commune with Mow (C) *v.*	mRRow(b4)
sofa, firm claw sharpener *n.*	pra^(b7)
softly, gently *a.*	m'ow(b2)
song *n.*	maow(d4)
speak in Fifth Maow (C) *v.*	maow(c7) miaow
speak in Second Maow (C) *v.*	maow(a7) miaow
squeak, say (nC) *v.*	aaa`(c4)
stir, mix, prepare; improve upon, adjust, knead, decorate; scratch; sharpen *v.*	truh(b4, c4)
stroke, worship through caress (nC) *v.*	Rup(c4)
stupid, to be; to beg pardon for not hearing (nC) v.	nrow(c4) rrow(b3)
swim, *v.*	praow(c4)(nC)
tail *n.*	rowb(b6)
take, *v.*	marow(c4)(nC)
talk, say (C) *v.*	miaow(b4)

task, divinely assigned duty/responsibility (C) *n.*	**maaw**(d4)
testicles *n.*	**mRRaow**(a3)
thank you (nC)	**ma` RRow**(a1)
thank you (C)	**mow**(a1) **mbruuh**(a1)
there *a.*	**nr'mow**(a1)
thing, object, idea, place *n.*	**marro**(a5)
think, imagine, dream *v.*	**miow**(b4, c4)
ticket *n.*	**muah**(c3)
titbit, snack *n.*	**mRRah**(a4)
to, for, at, from, off, etc.	**m`**
today *a.*	**meow**(d1)
toy *n.*	**^ra`**(b1)
tree *n.*	**breh**(b4)
tuna (fish) *n.*	**miew**(a2)
tuna (meat) *n.*	**miew**(a4)
understand, accept *v.*	**meow**(b4, c4)
unpleasant *a.*	**nmbruh**(f 7)
virtuous *a.*	**RRuh**(a5)
walk, move, *v.*	**mRaow**(c4)(nC)
wash, clean *v.*	**rro**(b4, c4)
water, *n.*	**pwah**(f7)
wet *a.*	**pwah**(c3)
when, nevertheless, and, but, however, who, which, etc.; the subordinate connector	**muh**(a7)
whiskers *n.*	**rrow**(b4)
winning, lucky *a.*	**mowrow**(c4)
wish, desire, need, want *v.*	**bRuh**(b4, c4)
with, by means of	**ruh**(b2)
work, do (nC) *v.*	**bra**(c4)
yes; indeed?	**moh**(a5)